Praise for
MEMORIES ETCHED IN POTT'RY

"In this charming memoir, Emory Jones takes us back to his great-uncle Cheever's pottery shop in 1958. When the day is done, you'll feel like you know Cheever Meaders and his wife, Arie, personally. That's because an artist from Atlanta, John Kollock, and his sweetheart, Nancy Rigg (later his wife), pay an imaginary visit. Their conversations make for a memorable day."
Billy Chism—former editor and publisher, White County News

"This book is a must for all interested in Georgia history as well as those who have a love for the art of "turning and burning" as it was done in the past. A word of caution: once you start reading, it is impossible to stop until the end."
William M. House—Attorney at Law and Avid Pottery Collector

"Emory has written a wonderful memoir that allows us to glimpse both Cheever and Arie Meaders as skilled potters and delightful people. One gets to understand the sadness in the changing times that made Cheever's life's calling obsolete.
Ann Banke—retired educator and lover of history

"Fess Parker, Joe the Rooster, Shooting Yankees from the Front Porch, Mule Measles, and Daisies on Pottery...heck...just read it, you'll love it."
Doug Dahlgren-Radio host and author of The SON Series

Memories Etched in Pott'ry

BECKY PEEBLES

Memories Etched in Pott'ry

The Cheever Meaders Story

by

Emory Jones

Legal review by William M. House
First Edition: July 2018
Printed in the United States of America
ISBN: 978-0-9887325-7-5

Cover art by John Kollock is provided courtesy of the
William M. House collection.

To My Aunt Barbara Meaders Allison
The Keeper of The Vase and the Sweetest Woman Ever

PREFACE

I remember the day Cheever Meaders died.

It happened on Thanksgiving morning 1967. I'd just turned seventeen.

When it comes to the past, the mind can be dishonest— even deceitful sometimes. But I checked the dates on the tombstone at Mossy Creek Church, and my mind told the truth about those.

I checked the dates for Granddaddy, too, while I was there. As my mind remembered, he died in 1965, two years before Cheever.

Granddaddy's name was Wiley. He was Cheever's oldest brother. I still missed that good man dreadfully in 1967. Maybe that's why Uncle Cheever's death hit me so hard. People I loved were leaving.

That, and the fact that when you're seventeen, nobody's supposed to die on Thanksgiving morning.

Before Granddaddy passed away, I lived with him and my grandmother in the southern end of North Georgia's White County. I'd lived with them off and on since I'd turned one.

When I turned six and started school, that arrangement became permanent. My mother lived there, too, and had since my father lost his life trying to save his friend from dying in a well. I was eleven months old when he and Bill Griffin died that day. That's another story for another book. Maybe.

As a boy, I thought everybody everywhere raised chickens, set out rabbit boxes in winter, and kept a cow or two for milk—everybody I knew did. We were country people, but no one ever told me.

The day Cheever died dawned damp, drizzly and foggy. It's funny I remember the weather, but I do. Maybe that misty fog was the reason the siren over on Highway 129 sounded so ethereal. Or maybe it really was ethereal.

In those days, when a siren's sound slipped in from some distant road, people went outside to suppose what calamity it decreed.

"It's coming from Cleveland," someone would say.

"No, no. It's way west of there and heading south. Old man Hulsey's likely had a heart attack."

We lived across a creek and two pastures from Cheever's place. So, on that Thanksgiving morning in 1967, we all knew where the ambulance stopped. The siren went silent at Cheever's house.

"It's likely bad," said my grandmother, Ruth, preparing me.

As she correctly supposed, that Thanksgiving siren did mark Cheever's final hour, in this world at least. A phone call soon confirmed that. Most of the nine families on our party line heard the news together.

Ever the working man, Cheever had been bringing in an armload of firewood when his heart failed. The caller—my mind won't pretend to remember who—said those sticks scattered around his woodstove when he fell.

We didn't have the Internet, Facebook or Twitter then, but tragic news spread about as fast via car horns, church bells, and those legendary party lines.

Cheever died in overalls that smelled of pipe tobacco, roasted peanuts, and earth. He would have been cradling that firewood in his left arm—the one that locked at the elbow when he fell from an apple tree as a boy. He was putting up a swing for his baby sister, Johnnie Mae, when that happened.

I never understood why somebody didn't set that arm right, but nobody did.

When I asked Grandmother about that, she said, "Well, there weren't many doctors around back then. Just the one down at Clermont, and folks wouldn't let him doctor a cow if they could help it."

Grandmother added, "Cheever's mama mighta' done more if she'd been there, but she was already dead and gone by then."

I guess they did the best they could.

With that bad arm, it's amazing that Cheever could turn clay at all, let alone become a master potter who produced dozens of churns a day in his prime. Once, when I was ill-mannered enough to ask Cheever about his arm, he scoffed and said he didn't remember it being any other way.

At one time, this spot at the southern end of White County, Georgia, had dozens of pottery shops like Cheever's. Shops like the one my grandfather closed when his two boys—my uncles—left to fight in WWII.

Handmade pottery was a vanishing trade, and by the mid-fifties, Cheever's shop was the only one left—along Mossy Creek, anyway.

For generations, the things Cheever and his brothers made were necessities. Folks literally could not live without them. By the time I came along, only a few people had a real *need* for pottery. Glass and tin cans were here. Folks looked down on anybody using old-fashioned pottery.

A few years later, Cheever's ware was on display at the Smithsonian Institution. It's true what they say: timing is everything.

The stories in this book all happened—in one way or another—at one time or another. Of course, I didn't really hear them all the same day the way it happens in this book.

I did hear them, though.

Most of these stories I heard sitting on my grandfather's lap which, by the way, is the best place for a youngster to hear old stories.

In other cases, I have taken literary license. For example, John Kollock and his future wife, Nancy, weren't there on that day in Cheever's shop depicted here in 1958.

They did meet Cheever and Arie in the late 1950's, but I wasn't around to see it. So, John and Nancy's conversations with Cheever and Arie in this book come strictly from my imagination. I didn't meet the Kollocks for another forty years.

I did spend a whole day in Cheever and Arie's shop in 1958, and I did ride that mule pretty much as described here.

Oh, and I did etch daisies on that little vase for Arie.

Some people—cousins and such—may remember these stories differently. But I don't think my mind is being too deceitful.

And if it is, how would I even know?

CHEEVER'S FAMILY TREE

Christopher Columbus Meaders (1808–1887) — Jane Garrison (1811–1893)

Barney, Jane, James Turner, David Albert, Wiley Parks, Lewis, Mary, John Milton

John Milton (1850–1943) — Mattie Lambert (1848–1896)

Camilla, Wiley, Caulder, Cleater, Casey, L.Q., Cheever, Elizabeth, Johnnie Mae

Cheever (1887–1967) —Arie Waldrop (1897–1989)

John, Lanier, Reggie, Edwin (Nub), Margie, Annie, Altha, Ruby

CHAPTER ONE

Cheever's Shop

I t was summer 1958.
I'd just turned eight the first time I spent a whole day in Uncle Cheever's pottery shop.

School was out, and my mother was going somewhere or other. She'd asked Aunt Arie, Uncle Cheever's wife, if they'd watch me while she was gone.

Nobody said "babysit," but that's what it amounted to.

Cheever and Arie probably weren't thrilled about having me there—they had work to do—but I was happy about it. What kid wouldn't be? With a dirt floor to play on, clay to mess with, and the nooks and crannies of a pottery yard to explore, the place was perfect—for a kid anyway.

Best of all, the old shop looked like a fort. And forts were much on my mind, thanks to my on-screen hero, Davy "Fess Parker" Crockett and Roy Rogers, King of the Cowboys!

I didn't have a six-gun, but I carried my trusty slingshot.

My best friend, Arnold Dyer, had one just like mine. His daddy helped us make them both. He'd cut an oak branch with a fork in it. Then he'd tied strips of rubber from an old inner-tube to the tops of the Y and laced a leather pouch to the other ends. That's where the rocks went.

Me and Arnold hadn't hunted anything with them yet. We'd practiced on cans, though. Cheever's "fort" would be a fine place to get more practice.

There was another reason I was happy. With a whole day at Cheever's shop, I was pretty sure he'd be grinding clay at some point. If he did, there was a good chance he'd let me ride his mule, Jason.

Jason pulled the big pole that turned the giant mixer. I had only been there for clay-grinding maybe two or three times, but each time, Cheever had set me on Jason's back for a short ride. He always did that when Mother was inside the shop talking with Arie.

Riding that mule was for sure the best thing about visiting there. It made me feel like Roy Rogers riding Trigger.

So, as soon as my mother drove away that morning in her 1955 Chevrolet Bel Air, I asked Cheever my main question. "Are you gonna be grinding clay today?"

"Plan to," he said, as I followed him and Aunt Arie into the shop.

I ran over to look inside the rain barrel under the drip of the roof. I had to stand on a pail to see, but it was pretty full.

On the way in, I kicked the cement block that held the tarpaper-covered door open. That left a scuff mark on my old lace-up Buster Brown shoes with the six-point fit.

They'd already gotten me through the school year, though—Mother would mind much.

"Can I ride Jason again when you do?"

Aunt Arie sighed as she sat down in her chair in front of a long, plank table against the shop's back wall. "Emory, you know good and well your mama said for you to stay off that mule."

I was trying to come up with something that might convince her Mother didn't *really* mean that when Uncle Cheever came up with something himself.

"His mama ain't here," he said, tapping tobacco from a red Prince Albert can into his pipe. He put the can in the pocket of his overalls. Then he walked over to the clay balls on a table behind the wheel. He'd been working up that clay when me and Mother got there a few minutes before.

"I reckon what she don't know won't hurt her," he said, lighting his pipe with a match. "Ain't that right, boy?"

Cheever went back to pounding the clay. "Wiley says she over-protects that little feller, anyhow—has ever since his daddy died."

"Pleeeease," I begged, looking at Arie with my most pitiful, I'm-almost-an-orphan expression. "I won't tell, I promise—I didn't last time."

Arie just sighed and went back to rolling little pieces of clay into grapes. I took that as a good sign.

"We'll go get that mule after-while, boy," said Cheever. Then he winked at me. "You can't ride him though."

I winked back, knowing a mule ride was in the bag. Arie noticed me and Cheever winking, so I winked at her, too. That way, she wouldn't think we were up to something.

The old shop didn't have many decorations. The main one was a *Peoples Bank* calendar with big white spaces for the dates. A pencil tied to a string hung beside it. That was in case anybody needed to write something on the calendar.

Hand-made scales for weighing clay hung high on the wall over the wheel and the wedging table. The scale was an old piece of fence rail with notches along the top. The rail lay across joists sticking out from the wall.

A flat piece of wood slinging from wire was where the clay went. A cluster of hammer heads, plow sweeps and points were wired together in a bunch. Cheever moved those from notch to notch tell how much clay he needed.

I didn't know how it worked exactly, but Cheever did.

A big, square fan hummed in front of the window by the door. The white power-cord that plugged into the outlet above it was stained with fly-specks.

The air from that fan felt good. Plus, it kept the flies away—some, anyhow.

As I think of that day, sixty years later, I see Cheever puffing on his corncob pipe while he presses the clay against the table with the heel of his hand. He pushes it over a wire, stretched between two posts to cut it into halves, then quarters. Then he pounds the pieces back together. Divide, unite, repeat. I remember it looked like fun to me.

In another corner, a potter's wheel sat inside a cluttered, mud-covered crib of boards.

A kick-paddle made the wheel turn. One end of that paddle went to some weird-shaped pieces of curved metal underneath. A chain bolted to the side held up the other end.

That chain had rubbed out a little place on the board from all the moving back and forth it did when Cheever kicked the foot-paddle.

On the back of the crib, sticking straight up, was a hinged piece of wood Cheever called a ball opener. He pulled that down to hollow out a hole in the clay, but just when he turned real big pieces.

Boards covered in wadded burlap made something like a seat against the wall. It let Cheever brace, more than sit, when he leaned against it to push the paddle with his leg.

Four windows, held open by sticks, let in light. They got help from a muddy lightbulb that dangled above the wheel. An old, kerosene lantern looked lonesome on a shelf all by itself. Its glass chimney stained black and cracked.

The shop smelled like dirt, peanuts, and pipe tobacco.

Wide, muddy planks made a shelf along the side closest to the door. That's where Cheever put the pottery when he'd finished turning it. When the shelf got full, he'd move everything somewhere else.

Sometimes, on a warm day, he and Arie took pieces outside to dry for a while.

I was sitting, taking my shoes off, when Arie got up from her chair. "Don't you think you oughta keep your shoes on?" she asked. "Your mama won't like you running around here barefoot."

"She won't care," I said, throwing my shoes and socks over by the wall. I took my slingshot off my belt and put it with them. I didn't want to get clay on it.

The dirt floor felt good and cool to my feet when I walked around.

"Well, it *is* awfully hot for shoes," Arie said. "But you'll have to put 'em back on before you go to the barn."

Then she picked up the littlest ball of clay off the wedging table. "Look here. I'm gonna make a special piece and let you pretty it up for me," she said, slapping the ball onto the wheel.

I watched her spin the little clay ball into a piece of pottery about six inches high.

While she did that, I squeezed some of the wet clay through my fingers. It felt smooth and soft and smelled like a creek after a big rain.

The pot was quickly made, and she pulled a wire under the bottom to keep it from sticking to the wheel.

"I'm gonna put this right over here," she said, picking it up carefully. "And you can decorate it for me." She sounded serious. Then she nodded towards a bench by the window. When I followed her to it, she turned a foot-tub upside down for me to sit on.

"Here you go," she said. "This'll make you a good place to work. It's by the window and close to the fan."

It was a good place to watch her and Cheever work, too. "What do you want me to put on this?" I asked, taking my job seriously.

Arie thought for a minute. "Daisies," she said. Then she picked up a little stick from the floor. "Use this to draw me some daisies."

Cheever and Arie worked without talking while I tried to draw flowers on that pot. It was hard. Plus, my little bench shook every time Cheever slammed one of his big clay balls down.

Sometimes, Arie hummed while she rolled bits of clay between her hands to make grapes. Then she'd stick them on the vase sitting in front of her. She made vines and leaves, too.

Every once in a while, Cheever handed me a peanut. He always had some in the bib pocket of his overalls. When he ran out, he'd get more from the pan Arie kept on her table.

Arie came over pretty often to check on my drawing. Each time, after looking at it, she'd wipe it off with her hand and say, "That's good, Emory, but you can do better. And remember, I need 'em on both sides."

Drawing on clay with a stick is hard. It's boring, too. Especially when there's a mule waiting for you.

Sitting back down, Arie pushed her glasses back to wipe her eyes with her apron. Then she leaned forward in that cane-back chair to stick another grape on one of the vases.

That didn't look like much fun. Still, it had to be more fun than drawing daisies on a wet pot with a stick. I wondered how many pieces Arie would decorate today. The shelves along the walls and in the back room looked full.

Over the hum of the fan, I could hear yard hens clucking and cackling as they scratched in the dirt. A crow cawed up at Cheever's cornfield behind the shop. Further away, another crow answered.

Inside, Cheever pointed with his chin towards the radio beside Arie. It only picked up one station—WRWH in Cleveland, 1350 on your dial. That's all we got on ours, too.

"Turn on that radio," he said. "It's about time for 'em to start playin' music."

"The news ain't over yet," said Arie. "But, I reckon it won't hurt none to hear some of it."

"Aw, they don't talk about nothin' but how nobody can find work n'more 'cause of the confounded recession," said Cheever. "I say anybody wantin' to work oughta come by here. I can find plenty for 'em to do."

"Yeah," said Arie, mainly to herself, "but most people want to get paid."

"What?" asked Cheever.

"Nothing," said Arie as she turned the radio on to let us hear a teenager's voice read the news. She turned it up pretty loud so Cheever could hear, too. He was hard of hearing like Granddaddy. Everybody said that ran in the family.

Except for me. I heard real good—even things I wasn't supposed to hear sometimes.

When Arie turned the radio on, the announcer sounded excited.

> "For sale: one dozen guineas, all laying. Five dollars for the lot. Call 2379 for details. That's all the items on today's Swap-Shop, folks. Remember, Swap-Shop is brought to you daily, Monday through Friday, by Nix Hardware on the square in Cleveland."

The announcer's voice grew serious. He cleared his throat.

> "In national news, President Eisenhower urges everyone to remain calm about Russia's launch of Sputnik Two. The President says the launch does not undercut our security and that he continues to remain confident regarding our country's defenses."

Cheever talked louder than the radio. "Did you hear about that poor little dog the Russians shot into space?"

I didn't know if he was talking to Arie or me, but she answered, so it must have been her.

"That was pitiful," she said.

"It was," said Cheever.

"I read somewhere it died," said Arie.

"What'd you say?" asked Cheever.

Arie reached over and turned the radio off. "The newspaper said that dog died."

Cheever heard that. "I reckon it would. Sendin' a dog into space oughta be against the law—less somebody's goin' along to look after it." Cheever looked at me. "Don't you think so, boy?"

I shrugged my shoulders. But, after that, all I could think about was that poor ole dog.

We all worked quietly for a few minutes; the hum of the fan the only noise.

Cheever still had that dog on his mind, too. "Looks to me like Crew-chef coulda' found somethin' else to send up beside a dog."

I thought so, too. Nobody would care much if they'd sent a possum into space. If the Russians were mean enough to do that to a dog, no wonder everybody was building a fallout shelter.

Cheever looked over at the radio again. "Turn that thing back on. Surely they've started playin' music by now."

But when Arie did, the announcer was still talking. He sounded real happy about the news he was telling now.

> "Last but not least, The Woodmen of the World organization is holding another Fourth of July Celebration in Cleveland next Saturday. As usual, the event's highlight will be the greased pig contest. I'll be bringing you all the action right here on WRWH!"

The Russians should have sent a pig into space instead of a dog. Nobody would miss a pig. That poor little dog was probably somebody's pet.

I was fixing to tell Cheever I hoped that dog bit ole Crew-chef when he put it in the spaceship when Arie turned the radio off. She tilted her head to listen to Lonzo bark at somebody outside, but in a friendly way.

"What'd you do that for?" asked Cheever.

"I thought I heard a car."

'What?"

"I heard a car."

"I didn't hear nothin'."

"I ain't surprised."

Cheever could hear me pretty good because I knew to talk loud—granddaddy couldn't hear good either.

Arie put the last grape on her vase, wiped her hands and whispered to me, "I reckon his ears are just for decoration nowadays."

I thought that was funny, but before I could whisper back to her, somebody knocked on the wall outside the shop door.

CHAPTER TWO

Cheever's Visitors

"Come on in," said Arie. "Door's open for a reason."

A well-dressed man in a blue shirt and khaki pants stood outside. He had a canvas bag slung over his shoulder. Behind him was a slender woman wearing a yellow dress and brown sandals.

"Hello. Mr. Meaders? Mrs. Meaders?" the man said, as he peered inside the shop. "Is this a bad time?"

Cheever looked up but kept pounding the clay. "Not as far as I know," he said. "You folks needin' some pott'ry?"

"Maybe. I'm John Kollock." Then he stood to one side to let the woman come in first. "This is my...ah, my friend, Nancy Rigg," he said. "We're from Atlanta."

I thought he looked a little embarrassed saying she was

his friend, but I didn't see why. She was pretty. Maybe he was embarrassed about being from the city.

"Pleased to meet you, Miss Rigg," said Arie. "You, too, Mr. Kollock."

"Oh," said the woman. "Please call me Nancy."

"And I'm just John," said the man.

The woman looked around and smiled. "This is wonderful," she said. "Exactly how I pictured it. It is such a pleasure to meet you both—finally."

I liked her. She was even prettier than my teacher, Miss Presley. I might marry her instead.

Everybody nodded to everybody else until the man slid the bag off his shoulder and stuck his hand out. Cheever stopped pounding the clay long enough to wipe his own hand off and shake Mr. Kollock's.

"I'm Cheever Meaders. This here's my wife, Arie." Then he looked at me and said, "That barefooted boy over there's Emory. He's my brother Wiley's grandson."

The man glanced at me, but then he looked back at Cheever. "I'm pleased to meet you," he said. "I've heard a lot about you and your pottery. You, too, Mrs. Meaders."

"You're famous," said Miss Nancy. She held up a magazine she'd brought with her. It had Uncle Cheever's picture on the front, standing behind some of his pottery.

"I've kept this magazine since it came out last year," she said. "I'm hoping you'll sign it for me while we're here."

We had a copy of that magazine at our house, but nobody had ever thought about asking Cheever to write his name on it.

"Let Arie do that," said Cheever. "She writes better'n I do."

Arie waved towards the end of her table. "Lay it down over there. I'll sign it after-while."

I wondered why she thought Cheever was famous. If he was, I don't think many people knew about it.

Miss Nancy cleaned off a place and put the magazine down. The man put his bag beside it. "Will this be all right here?" he asked, looking around like there might be a better place for it.

Nobody said anything, so he left it there.

"Ya say you're from Atlanta?" asked Cheever. "How do you make a livin' down there?"

"I'm an artist. I dabble some in theatre, too."

That made Arie look up. So, Mr. Kollock said, "I'm deeply interested in the history of this area, its people in particular."

When nobody said anything again, he did. "I have pretty deep roots here myself."

He seemed proud of that.

Cheever may not have heard him because he said, "An artist, are ya? We don't get many of them in here. What is it you heard about us?"

"We know Miss Marianne Kidd," said Miss Nancy. "She's the lady in that magazine article I brought. She's said some nice things about you both."

"That's why we're here," said the man. "I hope to meet all the mountain people featured in that article. We thought we'd start with you, since Miss Kidd spoke about you so highly."

Cheever reached inside his overalls pocket, took out a few peanuts and offered him one. "I always did have a weakness for flattery," he said. "Here, have some parched peanuts. They'll cure what ails ya."

"Parched?" The man acted like he might not know what that meant.

"Same as roasted," said Arie, pointing to the pan on the

table. "But get some from that-there pan; not the ones Cheever's had in his pocket all day."

I wondered why. I'd been eating peanuts from Cheever's pocket since I got here.

Mr. Kollock looked at the pan but didn't take any peanuts. "No, thank you," he said. "They smell good, but we ate a big lunch on the way up from Atlanta."

Cheever shrugged. "Suit yourself. They're mighty good, though—growed 'em myself."

Miss Nancy walked over to the pan and looked at it. "Well, in that case, I think we should try some. Don't you, John?"

She picked up the tin pan and held it out. Then she gave him a stern look and smiled at the same time. I thought only my mother could do that.

He took a peanut from the pan. Miss Nancy took three or four. She offered one to Aunt Arie, but Arie said, "No, thank you. I've been eatin' 'em all morning. I'll ruin my supper if I keep at it."

She was about to offer me one, too, but she saw the little pile Cheever had put on my bench, so she didn't.

"They *are* good," said the man, after shelling the peanut and popping it in his mouth. Then he looked around. I guess he was looking for a trashcan, but when he saw all the hulls around Cheever's boots, he dropped his on the floor, too.

"So, I hope you got my letter from last week, Mr. Meaders?"

Cheever didn't hear him. He just kept working. The man cleared his throat and said a little louder, "The letter explained that we hoped to drop by today. For a visit. And to spend some time watching you work—if you don't mind. For my research."

Cheever kept pounding the clay.

The man tried again. "I'd like to take some pictures, too, if that's all right."

When Cheever still didn't answer, Arie said, "You have to speak up." Then she stuck another grape on the vase. "You have a soft voice, and he's about as deaf as a fence post nowadays. Any Meaders over sixty is."

"I see," said Mr. Kollock, who cleared his throat real loud this time. He raised his voice some more and said, "We tried calling, but the operator couldn't find your number."

Cheever heard that because he said, "Yeah. That's a funny thing."

The man looked confused. "How so?"

"Well," said Cheever, "the telephone company won't give ya a number 'till ya rent a telephone from 'em. We ain't done that yet."

"Oh," he said. "I see."

Miss Nancy smiled. Then she bent over a little to watch Arie put grapes on the vase.

Cheever looked at Arie. "You know, I think we did get a letter from Atlanta last week. You never got around to readin' it to me, though."

That made Arie mad. "I did so! Right after supper Wednesday night. I declare, Cheever. You're gettin' so harda' hearing, you don't even *pretend* to listen to me n'more!"

"I do, too. Lots of times," said Cheever, going back to work.

"Well, I read it to you."

"Aw, I remember now," said Cheever. I thought he might be fibbing because, after that, he said, "Remind me again what it said."

Arie pointed at Mr. Kollock. "You tell him. You wrote it."

Mr. Kollock blinked a couple of times. "Well," he said,

"I wrote that we'd be coming up this way today—from Atlanta. That article piqued my interest in the mountain people even more. That's why I was hoping to spend some time with you— to learn more about your craft."

Cheever stopped pounding the clay and turned around. "I went to Atlanta one time. Arie did, too. We even rode that trolley-train they got down there. That thing beats all I've ever seen or heard of."

"In what way?" Mr. Kollock asked.

"For one thing," said Cheever. "Its overhead wires sparked somethin' awful ever' time we turned a corner. It's a wonder it ain't already burned somethin' down."

"I sure was proud to get home," said Arie. "I'll tell you that much."

"I understand," said Mr. Kollock. "I come up here to my grandmother's place pretty often. It's over near Clarkesville. Most times that place feels more like home than Atlanta does."

He looked at Miss Nancy. "We hope to live up here in the mountains full-time one day—I mean, at least I do."

She looked like she might not agree. I think Mr. Kollock noticed that because he kept looking at her.

He was still looking when Cheever asked, "Did you ever see that thing they call a cyclone-arama down there?"

"A what?" he asked.

"A cyclone-arama," said Cheever. "It's a big ole round thing with pictures painted on it."

Arie looked up and said, "He's talking about the cyclorama."

That got my attention! I'd seen the cyclorama myself. Mother took me there the week school let out.

Mr. Kollock had seen it, too, because he said, "Yes, sir. I have. Several times in fact."

"What's it like?" asked Cheever.

"I've seen it, too!" I blurted out before Mr. Kollock could answer. I knew it was rude, but I couldn't help myself. "It's big!" I said, holding my arms out real wide.

"That's wonderful," said Miss Nancy, smiling at me. "Why don't you tell us about it?"

All of a sudden, I felt bad that I'd seen the cyclorama when Uncle Cheever hadn't. "I just remember it was big, that's all," I said. Then I went back to drawing daisies.

"Well, it is a huge painting of the Battle of Atlanta," said Mr. Kollock. "You have to walk around in a big circle to see it all."

"And it's got Confederate soldiers painted on it?" asked Cheever.

"It does. Northern soldiers, too."

"Is it really forty feet tall?" Cheever asked.

"At least."

"Well, I guess you'd know," said Cheever. "What with you being an artist and all." Then he added, "You know, my pa might be painted on that thing somewhere. He claimed he was down there when all that fightin' went on."

Mr. Kollock glanced at Miss Nancy. "Well...I don't suppose they had room to put every person on it who was actually there."

When Cheever looked disappointed, he said, "But you never know."

Miss Nancy smiled at Cheever. "Maybe you can go down there again sometime and see for yourself," she said.

Cheever and Arie both laughed. "Naw," said Cheever. "Like I said, we already been to Atlanta. Don't plan on going back, either. Even if Pa *is* painted on that thing."

Now that I thought about it, one of those people painted on the cyclorama did look like Cheever and Granddaddy's pa. I'd better tell them that later.

"You say your given name's John?" Cheever asked.

"That's right. John Kollock. I'll try not to get in your way if you can let us watch you work for a little while. And maybe ask a few questions?"

Cheever lit his pipe again. "You Baptist, John?" he asked.

"Am I what?"

"Baptist."

"No. Why?"

"I's hoping you was. Ya see I'm bad to give out nicknames, and since you look sorta' like a preacher, I's gonna call you John the Baptist. That won't work though, will it?"

"I guess not," he said. "I'm sorry."

"Don't be," said Cheever. "I could call you 'Preacher,' but since you're an artist and all, I think I'll call you Painter Man."

Cheever took his pipe out and looked at the man. "Does that suit you? You tell the truth now, 'cause I never was one ta give a man a new name he didn't like—at least a little."

Mr. Kollock looked at Miss Nancy, who ducked her head like she didn't want to look at him. "What do you think, Nancy?"

She laughed and put her hand on his shoulder. She looked him right in the face and said, "I like Painter Man. In fact, I think it's a perfect nickname for you—for today, anyway."

Then she looked at me and asked, "Don't you think so, Emory?"

I nodded. But I'd get in trouble if I called him that—I better just call him, Mr. John.

Cheever pointed to two empty chairs and motioned for them to sit. Miss Nancy sat down in the one close to Arie. Mr. John moved his chair over by the wheel, but he didn't sit in it. He just put his hands on the chair's back and watched Cheever carry over a ball of clay.

Cheever sat that ball beside the ones he'd already brought. Then he took more clay over to Arie's table and plopped it down by her. "There you go," he said. "There's enough mud there to make grapes for a month."

Then he slapped his clay onto the wheel so hard it scared a hen pecking by the door.

Cheever struck a match and lit his pipe again. Then he braced against the wall-seat, put both hands around the clay and started pushing the kick-wheel back and forth with his foot.

Mr. John watched Cheever for a minute. "What were you doing with that clay over there on the table when we got here?" he asked.

"I's wedging it," said Cheever, without looking up. "Gettin' the air and hard places out. Gotta do that before you can do much with it on this-here wheel. Ya weigh it first to get the right amount of clay, and then you wedge it and ball it up. Want to try your hand? There's more clay over there if you do."

Mr. John looked down at his shirt. "Maybe later."

Cheever glanced up. "You're welcome to stand there," he said. "But I'm fixin' to splash water. It's liable to get all over you."

Cheever took one hand off the clay and cupped a handful of water from a little bucket by the wheel. When it splashed onto the clay, some of it did get on Mr. John's shirt, even though he'd backed up a bit. But he didn't seem to mind much.

"That's all right," he said. "I took a pottery course in art school. I know it's messy work."

"Well then," said Cheever, pulling the clay into the

shape of a pitcher. "You can tell me if I'm doin' this right. I never had no formal trainin'."

"Oh, no," said Mr. John. "I didn't mean to imply…"

Miss Nancy got up from her chair and came over to watch Cheever work. She didn't care much about the mud either.

Cheever liked having them watch because he started showin' off a little. He picked up the little piece of flat wood he called his chip. He ran it up the side of the piece real fast to smooth the clay out while it turned.

He splashed more water than he usually did, too.

I went over to look.

I still feel it now. It was like magic. You never know what the clay is becoming. Just as you decide that wet spinning glob is going to be a short bowl, Cheever moves his hands some, and it turns into a tall pitcher. I think he sometimes changes his mind on purpose to see me react, because then he smiles. Cheever reaches for the wire, pulls it taut with the end sticks. He gives the kick-wheel one last push and lets the wire separate his newest creation from the surface. The whir of that wheel—the clank of the treadle—the smell of that clay—is still in my mind today.

"And that's how it's done," he said, cutting the new piece off and putting it on the planks beside him.

That tickled Miss Nancy. "I can't believe how quickly you did that," she said. "It would have taken me a month!"

Cheever puffed on his pipe. "Well, it may be a month 'fore it's ready to sell," he said. "I'll put a handle on it after-while. Arie's gonna put some grapes or flowers on it, too, one or the other. Then we gotta glaze it and fire it. It takes a while."

"I'll dip that one in my new glaze," said Arie, looking over at the pitcher. "Bristol, they call it. It fires up real pretty—lots nicer than that old tobacco-spit green Cheever favors."

Arie motioned towards Miss Nancy. "Sit back down here by me." When she did, Arie said, "This is a real nice cookie jar I'm working on. So, I'm gonna put grapes on all four sides of it."

Miss Nancy looked like she didn't understand, so Arie said, "Sometimes I put 'em on three sides, or maybe just two. They'll fetch the same price either way, but they're nicer with four."

Arie pointed to an old apron hanging by the door to the back room. "I'd put on that apron over there if I was you. In a pottery shop, you'll get dirty just watchin'."

Miss Nancy went over, put the apron on and came back to sit down. I wondered if Arie was going to make her work like she did me. Probably not.

"Do you mind if I take a few pictures, Mr. Meaders?" Mr. John asked, getting a camera out of his bag.

"Go ahead on," said Cheever, "if you don't think I'll break your camera." I think he was glad about getting his picture made, though.

Mr. John was about to ask Arie if he could take her picture, too. Before he could, she said, "Law, no! Don't you dare point that thing at me—I'm a mess."

He pointed his camera at the wheel, but Cheever said, "Wait a minute. If you're gonna take my picture, I need ta be turnin' something bigger'n a vase."

Cheever went to the wedging table, picked up the biggest ball of clay there and took it to the wheel. "I'll turn a four-gallon churn for ya," he said. "That'll make better pictures."

"That looks heavy," said Mr. John, looking at the clay.

"Pshaw," said Cheever. "It just takes a few pounds to make a four-gallon churn. The ball for an eight-gallon piece is the one that gets heavy."

"Do you just guess at how much clay you need?"

"I can tell pretty good. But I weigh 'em out on that contraption over there when I need to be exact." He nodded towards the homemade scales.

When Cheever made the wheel start spinning again, he pulled the ball-opener down to make a hole in the clay. When that was done, he pulled some up to make the top of the churn. Then he cut that part off with his wood chip and used both hands to sit it on the shelf.

This seemed to surprise Mr. John. "Why do you do it that way?" he asked. "Don't you make churns in one piece, like everything else?"

"Naw," said Cheever. "My ole arm won't let me reach to the bottom, so I piece my churns."

"Piece?"

"Yeah. I pull it up a-ways and put a lip on it. I set that part off and finish the rest. After-while, I'll put the two back together."

"Interesting."

"It's just how I learned to do it," said Cheever. "My boy, Lanier, makes 'em the same way, and they ain't nothin' wrong with his arm."

While Cheever was making that churn, Mr. John moved around him, pointing his camera. He took a picture from every place he could. He even stood on the chair to make one. I thought he might fall, but he didn't.

One time, when Arie wasn't looking, he took one of her, too.

When he had enough pictures, he put the camera back in his bag. Then he took out a notebook and a pencil.

"As I wrote in that letter, I've already read quite a bit about your family as background for a project or two I hope to do one day. I'd like to hear more about all that from you, though—direct from the horse's mouth, so to speak."

Cheever splashed more water on the clay. "I hope you don't believe too much of what's been said—about me, anyhow."

"Oh, it's all been good. Mostly."

Cheever gave the paddle one last kick, which made it squeak real loud. "Mostly?" he asked. "You must not be talkin' to the right people."

Mr. John laughed. "I think I am. Now, let's see—your children are John, Lanier, Reggie, Edwin, Margie, Annie, Altha, and Ruby. Is that accurate?"

"That don't sound right," said Cheever, taking down a set of metal lifters from the wall. He opened them like jaws and fitted them around the bottom of the churn. Then he used the handles on each side to lift it off the wheel and put it on the shelf.

"It doesn't?" asked Mr. John. "I mean...that's what I have written down here. This is from the courthouse records..."

Arie wiped her hands and leaned back to look at the grape cluster she'd just now finished. "He thinks of 'em as Rufus, Bence, Reg, Nub, Touch-Me-Not, Black-Eyes, Dootsy, and Peep-Peep."

Mr. John looked confused. "Really?" he asked, sitting down in the chair real slow.

Arie rolled her eyes. "Cheever's bad to give out nicknames. Remember?"

"Oh, yes," he said. "Of course."

Miss Nancy looked closely at Arie's grapes. "Does he have a nickname for you, Mrs. Meaders?" she asked.

"He better not," said Arie, reaching for another piece to decorate.

"Why not?" Miss Nancy asked.

Cheever had just put some more clay on the wheel. He looked up. "You are right about it bein' hot. Go stand in front of that fan a-while—that'll cool you down some."

I watched to see if she could tell he hadn't heard her right.

Miss Nancy looked directly at Cheever and spoke louder. "Oh, I wasn't complaining about the heat. Your wife was just explaining that you don't have a nickname for her."

Cheever looked down at the clay. I could already tell it was going to be a pitcher—at least I thought so. "I have one for my dog, though," he said, pumping the kick-wheel. "It's Lonzo."

"Lonzo?" said Mr. John.

"Yeah," said Cheever. "His real name's Napoleon, but I nicknamed him Lonzo. Suits him better, don't ya think?"

"Actually, I do," said Mr. John. "When he greeted us outside a while ago, I thought he looked more like a Lonzo than a Napoleon."

"You got a good eye," Cheever said.

Cheever had two nicknames for me. One was *Embo*, and the other was *boy*. He called me both names pretty often, but I liked Embo best.

While they were talking, I went over and looked out the door at Lonzo. He was laying in the shade of the kiln, panting. His ears flicked forward every time Cheever said his name.

I liked Lonzo. He was a little sandy colored dog with three white paws.

Mr. John cleared his throat and looked at his notebook. "Do you mind if I ask a few questions now?"

"Ask away, Painter Man," said Cheever. "But I'm a day late and a dollar short, so I gotta keep goin'."

Arie broke off some more clay. "Cheever, you ought not

change a man's name," she said. "Not the first time you meet him, anyhow."

"Why not?" asked Cheever. He looked back over his shoulder. "Painter Man suits him."

Cheever splashed more water onto the clay he'd put on the wheel. Then he cupped his hands around the spinning mud.

Mr. John wrote something down and said, "Mr. Meaders, you can call me anything you like as long as you'll tell me a bit about your family. Is that a deal?"

"I reckon so," said Cheever. "I might remember more if you was gonna be buyin' some pott'ry, though."

Arie didn't think he should have said that because she said, "Cheever!" real loud and gave him a stern look. She didn't smile either.

"Oh, we do want to buy a piece or two of your pottery," said Miss Nancy. "But, probably not this trip. John has the car packed full."

"Aw-right then," said Cheever, as he took his newest pitcher—I was right about that—off the wheel and put it on the boards beside him. Then he centered another ball of clay on the wheel. "Ask away, Painter Man."

Mr. John glanced down at his notebook. "I may have this wrong," he said. "I have your brothers as Wiley, Cleater, Caulder, Casey, and L.Q. Is that correct?"

"That's right," Cheever said, as he pulled the clay up.

Mr. John looked like he'd expected Cheever not to agree with him. "No nicknames for them?" he asked.

"What kinda' feller would nickname his brothers?" asked Cheever.

"I'm not sure," said Mr. John. Then he changed the subject. "Your three sisters are Camilla, Elizabeth, and Johnnie Mae?"

Cheever pushed his thumbs into the clay. "Camilla and Johnnie Mae sound right. I don't recall havin' a sister named Elizabeth."

"He means Lizzie," said Arie, without looking up.

Cheever acted surprised.

"Oh, yeah," he said. "That's the first time I've heard Lizzie called Elizabeth in seventy years. Don't sound right."

I liked Aunt Lizzie. She always had a fried apple pie for me, and she knew how to shoot snakes at the creek. But it did sound funny to hear somebody call her Elizabeth.

"Was Lizzie her nickname?"

"Naw. It's short for Elizabeth," said Cheever.

"I see. Well then, can you tell me anything more about those three?"

"I can," said Cheever. He didn't say anything else.

When Mr. John cleared his throat, Arie said, "Well, are you gonna?"

"Am I gonna what?" asked Cheever.

"Tell him more about your sisters."

"He didn't ask me to."

"Yes, he did."

"No. He asked me if I *could* tell him more about my sisters."

Cheever was right. That was what he'd asked all right.

"Tell him anyway," said Arie.

Cheever let the wheel stop turning and took the pipe out of his mouth. He looked at it for a minute and said, "Lizzie and Camilla never married. Camilla's dead now. Lizzie still lives over there in that old house." He pointed across the road with his pipe.

"What did they do for a living?" asked Mr. John, writing in his notebook.

Cheever put his pipe back in his mouth and puffed on it.

"Lizzie taught school and piddled some here at the shop. Camilla kept house for Pa, and she was a good hand at sellin' pott'ry. She never made any, though. None of the girls did."

Miss Nancy looked at Arie and asked, "So, Johnnie Mae, the youngest, was the only one to ever marry and leave home?"

"Yeah," said Arie. "I reckon she wanted to trade paper shades for curtains."

Miss Nancy smiled.

Arie looked like she wanted to say something else about Johnnie Mae. After a moment, she did.

"I remember after Johnnie Mae moved to Gainesville, Lizzie asked her how she liked livin' in town."

"What did she say?" asked Miss Nancy.

"Well," said Arie. "Johnnie Mae said it was fine except that some folks down there walked down the street like they owned the left side and was thinkin' seriously about buying the right."

Everybody laughed but me. I didn't even know you could buy a sidewalk. I wondered what one cost.

"I can assure you," said Miss Nancy, "that malady is even more widespread in Atlanta."

Mr. John wrote that sidewalk story down. Then he asked Cheever, "What are you willing to tell me about yourself, Mr. Meaders?"

"Not much," said Cheever, starting the wheel spinning again. "Ain't much to tell."

Down on the road, a car honked its horn as it drove by. Arie looked out the door. "Did you see who it was?"

"Naw," said Cheever. He stopped pumping the kick-paddle and looked out the door. "It sounded like Julian Dixon's ole car. The dog didn't bark, so he musta known 'em." Then he went back to spinning the clay.

Mr. John scooted his chair closer. "Mr. Meaders? May I ask when you were born?"

"To tell the truth, I don't remember much about that," said Cheever. "That's because I's born at such a young age, I reckon. Especially for a baby."

He didn't wink at me when he said that, but I knew he was teasing. I think Mr. John did, too.

"You're not going to believe this," he said, "but so was I. Can we start with the year and place that happened?"

"For you or for me?" asked Cheever.

Arie and Miss Nancy both grinned.

"For you," said Mr. John. "I have all the information I need about me."

"Aw-right then," said Cheever, splashing water on the clay as it turned. "I's born in eighteen hundred and eighty-seven over there in that old house across the road, and a pretty good feller yet. I reckon they's still a whole lotta work left in this old hide."

"I do believe there is." Mr. John said, writing fast again. "Can you tell me how and when this pottery shop got started?"

"I can," said Cheever, splashing more water. "The question is whether or not I will." Then he winked at me.

"Oh, don't worry about that," said Arie, rolling another clay grape between her hands. "He will."

Mr. John got up and went over to his bag and put his notebook in it. "I'd appreciate if you would," he said. Then he took out a pad like real artists draw on. "Do you mind if I make a few sketches while we talk? I think that might work better than taking notes."

Cheever looked at the drawing pad. "You like to draw, do you?"

Mr. John nodded yes.

"Are ya any good at it?" asked Cheever.

"Well, I make a living at it in Atlanta," He sat down again. "I'm not sure I could here in the hills, though."

"You can't ever tell," said Cheever, as he put the pitcher he'd just turned on the shelf by the wheel. Then he took his pipe out of his mouth and tapped some more tobacco into it. "Folks pay me to play in this ole mud, so I reckon we're about even."

I wondered if anybody would pay me to draw something. I came second in the art contest at school. Chris Black came in first. Chris drew a football. I drew an airplane. It was easy—not like working on clay.

Mr. John was about to draw on his pad some more when Cheever started wiping his hands off on a rag.

He looked at me and said, "I'm about outta clay, Embo. You 'bout ready to quit drawin' flowers and go get that mule?"

Mr. John seemed surprised. I guess he'd planned on drawing a picture of Cheever at the wheel.

Arie looked up. "Cheever, you know what Emory's mama said."

"Aw, I'm too hard of hearin' to say what it was," he said, as he took off his apron. "But it's awful hard to keep a boy off a mule. I never had much luck keeping girls off one either."

"Well, at least put your shoes on," Arie said to me.

"Do I have to?" I begged.

"You do," she said.

I looked at Cheever. He shrugged. Then he hung his apron on a nail. "You wanna come with us, Painter Man?"

Mr. John looked at Miss Nancy. "Is that all right with you?"

"It's fine with me, Painter Man," she said, laughing. "I'll

stay here and chat with Mrs. Meaders. Just promise me you'll stay off that mule."

"I promise," he said. Then he put his drawing pad back in the bag and took out his camera, slinging it over his shoulder by the strap.

"Be careful with the boy," said Arie, as the two men went out the door.

I put my shoes and socks on as fast as I could. Then I stuck my slingshot in my belt and ran outside.

I was hoping Miss Nancy would come with us, but she didn't.

CHAPTER THREE

Cheever's Path

When I got outside, I thought I'd have to run down the trail to catch up. I didn't, though because Cheever and Mr. John were just standing there.

Lonzo jumped up to lick my face. I didn't mind, but Cheever made him get down. Then he took his pipe out of his mouth, stood in the sunshine for a moment and stretched his arms wide. Lonzo stretched, too.

It was bright outside. Cheever put on the cap he'd grabbed on the way out and pulled its bill down low to shade his eyes.

"The barn's down that way," he said, pointing with his pipe to the path. I knew that trail well. It ran through the pine trees above the highway, down to the house and on to the barn where the mule was.

I was in a hurry, but Mr. John wasn't. Cheever didn't seem to care much one way or the other. So, Mr. John started looking around the yard.

The place had so much to see, it was hard to look at everything. But Mr. John tried. First, he looked at the two old wooden tables that leaned together like they were holding each other up. They also held up pitchers, churns, and vases of all sizes—some glazed, some not.

Lots of other pottery sat on the ground all over the yard. Mr. John wanted to look at everything.

Cheever stood there, puffing on his pipe, and let him look. I sat down and petted Lonzo. I let him lick my face when nobody was looking.

Mr. John's brown car sat alongside the road by the rock chimney. When Granddaddy was young, he helped build that. It used to be part of what he called *the old shop*.

Mr. John looked at that chimney for a long time. Then he took its picture.

After that, he walked over to Cheever's pugmill. The old thing had a big, gray overhead pole held up at each end by three posts leaned together. Cheever had nailed planks around those to keep everything in place.

The high pole balanced on top of another one sticking out of a barrel-like thing about three feet tall. That's where Cheever put the clay. The pole in the barrel had pegs pounded into it so it acted like a big wooden mixer. It mixed the clay up good.

Mr. John took a picture of that. When he finished looking at the pugmill, he went over to the squatty old brick kiln and got down on one knee in front of the little arched door. It was the only way in or out.

I decided not to tell him about the dragon.

Arnold Dyer was the only one I'd told about the dragon

that lived in Cheever's kiln. Cheever fed him every few weeks, and when he did, that dragon breathed fire up through the kiln's chimney so high you could see it all the way to our house.

Rusty old tin made a roof over the dragon's house. More sheets of tin stretched out on both sides. They looked like a hen's wings when she's about ready to sit on a nest.

Cheever kept stacks of sawmill slabs under those two wings. They were for the dragon.

Mr. John still wasn't ready to leave yet. You'd think he'd never seen a pottery yard before.

Just when I thought he was finished, he put another roll of film in his camera and started taking more pictures. He even took one of the chickens.

While he was doing that, I showed my slingshot to Lonzo. Then I got up and walked around some.

There was something shiny on the ground over by the kiln, so I went to see what it was. It was a piece of tin, and it looked like a good target. At least I'd get in some practice while Mr. John looked around.

I walked back a few feet, picked up a rock and put it in the leather pouch at the end of my slingshot.

But, just as I pulled back the rubber and let that rock fly, Lonzo jumped up to lick my face again. Smash! That rock flew right into one of Aunt Arie's little bowls about ten feet away!

The fan in the shop was humming too loud for her to hear that pot break. But Cheever did.

I felt so bad, and a little scared, too. Aunt Arie might be mad at me.

"I didn't mean to," I said to Cheever. "Lonzo jumped up on me by mistake. I'm sorry."

Cheever just shook his head. He walked to the busted

bowl and picked it up. He put his finger to his lips to tell me to be quiet. Then he went to the kiln door and tossed the pieces inside.

"She won't miss it," he said, walking over to me. When he held out his hand, I handed him the slingshot. He put it in his pocket and puffed some on his pipe.

I sat back down with the dog. I still felt bad, and I think he did, too.

Mr. John had been exploring up behind the shop, so I don't think he heard me break Aunt Arie's bowl.

At last, he swung his camera over his shoulder. "You were going to tell me how you and your brothers got into the pottery business," he said to Cheever.

"I was," said Cheever, starting down the path. Finally!

Me and Lonzo ran on ahead, till Cheever hollered, "Don't get off the trail, boy. And watch for snakes. I killed a copperhead up there last week as big as your arm."

I decided to stay on the path. Granddaddy said rattlesnakes were out, too. I was sorta' glad I had shoes on.

I thought sure we were on the way to the barn. But when I looked back, the two men had stopped to talk some more. So, I walked back to them and sat down again. Lonzo lay down next to me.

"My pa built this shop," Cheever was saying, as he puffed on his pipe. "Helped do it, anyhow. My older brothers did all the work."

He stood looking back at the tarpaper-covered building, not saying anything—thinking some. "I's just four or five then, so I sorta growed up in it. Worked here my whole life. Never done nothin' else."

For a minute, I thought Cheever seemed sad about that.

Then he got happy again. "My first memories were of this place," he said. "When I was little, I'd get up on that head block I's workin' on back there, and my brothers would spin me around. Sounds sorta foolish now, looking back on things like that. 'Course, our young'uns did that, too."

I guess I seemed bored because Cheever looked at me. "You want to see somethin', Embo?"

I nodded quickly, knowing it would likely be something good. You never knew what Cheever might come up with.

He looked back at the red rooster scratching beside the shop wall. "You see that rooster there?"

I looked where he was pointing and nodded.

"He'll crow if I tell him to."

"No, he won't," I said. I was sure he was fooling again.

"Yes, he will. Watch this."

Cheever cupped his hands around his mouth and hollered, "Crow, Joe!" That rooster crowed just like Cheever said he would. It surprised me so much I stood up! It surprised Mr. John, too.

Arnold Dyer wasn't going to believe this!

Then Cheever hollered, "Crow, Joe," and the rooster crowed again! I'd heard roosters crow all my life. But this was the first time I'd heard one do it because somebody told it to!

"Can I try?" I asked.

"It's a free country," said Cheever. "Remember, you gotta be smarter'n a chicken to make one crow when ya tell it to."

I knew I was smarter than a chicken. So, I cupped my hands and hollered, "Crow, Joe!"

But ole Joe didn't crow. He just cocked his head and pecked at one of the hens. Then he went back to his scratching.

"You ain't holdin' your mouth right," said Cheever. "Here, watch me." Cheever tilted his head and pulled his lip back. Then he stood on one foot and waved the other one around in the air.

"Try doin' it that way."

I spent the next few minutes balancing on one foot, pulling my lips back and trying to get ole Joe to crow. He never did, though, and finally, I gave up.

Cheever patted my head. "Let's go to the barn, boy," he said. "I thought you was in a hurry to get that mule."

As we started down the trail again, Cheever put his hand on my back. "Don't worry too much about ole Joe," he said. He won't hardly crow for nobody 'cept me. I taught him how right after he hatched."

Then Cheever stopped. He looked like he'd just thought of something. "Did you know Christopher Columbus was my granddaddy?"

That made me stop, too. Even Lonzo looked up at Cheever. He might be fooling again, but if Christopher Columbus *was* his granddaddy, that made me kin to him, too.

Arnold Dyer was always talking about how his great-great-granddaddy invented the airplane before the Wright brothers did. Being kin to Christopher Columbus would top even that.

It sure did impress Mr. John. "*The* Christopher Columbus?" he asked. "You don't look that old."

"Well," said Cheever. "He was Christopher Columbus Meaders."

Aw, shoot. Cheever was fooling again. I'd have to come up with something else to top Arnold's airplane story.

"Christopher Columbus Meaders had a pa who fought in the war of eighteen and twelve," said Cheever. "The govmeant gave him land down here for doin' that. That's how come us to be here and not in Virginia."

Since I wasn't kin to Christopher Columbus, me and Lonzo started looking around for a stick to throw. But I kept half an ear open in case Cheever said something interesting again.

"Do you remember Christopher Columbus Meaders?" Mr. John asked.

"Naw. I's less'n a year old when Grandpa died," said Cheever. "I sorta remember Grandma, though. I recall her sittin' on the porch of that big house they had down below here, readin' her Bible. That was the finest house you ever saw."

"So, your grandfather was well off?"

Cheever looked down at his overalls. "Yeah. You couldn't tell it by looking at his grandson, could ya?"

"Oh, you look like you're doing all right to me."

"Not like Grandpa, though. He was the richest feller in forty miles. I don't know how much land he had, but it was considerable." Cheever waved his good arm in a circle. "He owned most ever' thing around here."

"What happened?"

Cheever snorted. "The War Between the States happened, that's what!"

I looked at his face. He was mad.

"There wasn't much fightin' in these parts," said Mr. John. "Still, I know it had a devastating effect."

"You're telling me it did," said Cheever. "After the war was over, ever' body around here was poor as Job's turkey. Grandpa still had his land, but it waddn't worth nothin' — just somethin' to pay taxes on."

"It was the same over in Habersham County," Mr. John said. "I've heard my grandmother tell stories about how bad those times were for our family."

"Yeah," agreed Cheever. "From the time that war ended

till I's grown, folks around here had a hard time of it. They'd-a starved if hadn't been for rabbits and such."

"Rabbits?"

"Yeah," said Cheever. "And I learned early on that squirrel dumplings taste pretty good when you're hungry. Poke sallet, too."

Mr. John looked like he wasn't sure about that. "Well," he said, "I hear pokeweed is full of iron, so it might be good for you. But isn't it poisonous?"

"It can be," admitted Cheever, "But not if ya pick it in the spring and boil it three times in different water. Anyhow, the roots and berries are where most of the poison is."

Poison? I guessed I better tell Arnold about that. Me and him used poke berries for war paint sometimes.

"Poke sallet tastes too good to hurt a'body much," said Cheever. "Especially how Arie cooks it; scrambled up in eggs and bacon grease. It's mighty tasty."

I didn't agree with Cheever on that. Polk salad smelled bad when Grandmother cooked it and tasted even worse.

"I'll have to try it sometime," said Mr. John. "Getting back to our subject, I take it the Meaders men all fought on the Confederate side?"

"They did," said Cheever. "A few from here took the Northern view. Lots more hid out in the woods to keep from fighting for either one."

I was getting ready to throw the stick I'd found for Lonzo. But just then a rabbit jumped out from under a log, and he ran off after it. So, I stood there, looking back at Cheever and Mr. John, waiting for them to catch up.

Adults sure can be slow.

"Four of Pa's brothers joined up the same day," Cheever said as they caught up to me.

"The same day?"

"Yep." Cheever sounded proud of that. "They joined the Twenty-Fourth Georgia Infantry. Two of our cousins from Cleveland joined up with 'em. 'Course, they's all older'n Pa. He was the baby boy."

"Do you know what happened to them?" Mr. John asked.

Cheever reached into his bib pocket and took out some peanuts. "Two of 'em made it home; two of 'em didn't."

"I suppose they were killed?"

"I reckon so," said Cheever, stopping to listen at Lonzo chase the rabbit. "Don't you hurt that rabbit, Lonzo!" he hollered at him. "It ain't done nothin' to you."

Cheever started talking about the war again. "Grandpa got a letter sayin' Uncle James died in the fightin' around Gettysburg. They never did hear what happened to Uncle Wiley. I reckon he's the one my oldest brother is named for."

So that's how Granddaddy got his name. I didn't know that. I wonder if he did.

Just then, Mr. John stopped and looked up the trail towards his car, which was still in sight since we hadn't gone far. "Wait a moment," he said. "I might be able to shed some light on that."

Then he started trotting back towards the shop, talking over his shoulder as he went. "Excuse me for a minute while I get something out of my car."

"I wonder what he's going for?" asked Cheever.

I didn't know, and I didn't care. All I knew was that he was going in the wrong direction.

"Let's you and me sit down here and wait on him," said Cheever, looking at the log the rabbit had jumped out from under. He kicked it hard with the bottom of his foot to see if there was a snake under it. Nothing rattled, so we sat down.

Lonzo came back without the rabbit. He was panting pretty hard, so I let him put his head in my lap while we waited for Mr. John.

We heard the car trunk slam shut. Then we saw him start back. He walked real slow though. That's because he was thumbing through a big gray book.

"Whatcha got there?" Cheever asked when Mr. John got close enough.

"It's a roster of Georgia's Confederate soldiers," said Mr. John, sitting down on the log. "It amuses Nancy that I keep historical information like this in my car. But you never know when something like this book might come in handy."

Just then, a June bug buzzed by.

"Catch it, boy!" said Cheever. "We'll tie a string around its leg, and let it buzz around our heads for a while."

I grabbed at the June bug but missed. Shoot. Cheever looked disappointed.

Mr. John kept turning the pages. Then he looked like he'd found something. "Was your uncle's name Wiley *Parks* Meaders?"

"That's right. Why?"

Mr. John shooed a fly away and tapped the page with his finger. "Here it is. Right here. This lists Private Wiley Parks Meaders as having died in Chimborazo Hospital, Richmond, Virginia, on the twenty-fourth of June, 1864."

"Well, I'll swanee," said Cheever, looking down at the book. "Does it say what killed him?"

Mr. John looked down at the book again. "The cause of death is listed here as *vulnus laceration*."

"Sounds like a bad way to go," said Cheever.

I thought so, too.

Mr. John looked like he was thinking. "Yes, it probably was. *Vulnus laceration* is Latin for a traumatic injury. In this case, most likely a gunshot."

"Well, they was lots of that goin' around back then," said Cheever. When Mr. John tried to hand his book to him, Cheever pretended he was thinking about something else.

So, Mr. John put the book back in his lap and scratched his head. "I'm pretty sure June twenty-fourth was two or three weeks after the Battle of the Wilderness in Virginia. Considering the timing and the closeness of that hospital, I bet he was wounded there and died later in Richmond."

Cheever studied Mr. John. "Pa wondered what happened to his brother, Wiley Parks, all his life," he said. "I wish he could'a known that before he died."

Cheever looked back at the old house across the road for a minute.

Mr. John seemed pleased. "Well, I'm glad I could help with that." Then he looked at the book again. "Didn't you say your father was in the Confederate Army, too?"

He started flipping pages again. In a minute, he looked up and said, "I don't see his name here."

"Ah, Pa claimed he was," said Cheever. "Like I said when we was talkin' about that cyclo-whatcha-may-call it. But I don't know if he was or not. He talked about ridin' the train down to Atlanta and back, but I don't think they ever gave him a gun. He was just eleven when the war broke out."

I was pretty sure he *was* in that Atlanta fight, since I'd plainly seen him painted on the cyclorama.

Mr. John started thinking in his head again. "Your father would have only been fourteen during the Atlanta siege," he said. "Still, that was quite often old enough for the Home Guard."

"I reckon so," said Cheever. Then it seemed like he wanted to take up for his pa. "I'll tell you one thing Pa did," he said. "He stole a Yankee saddle."

"He stole a saddle?" Mr. John seeming surprised. "From the Union Army? Did that happen in Atlanta?"

I knew about that saddle; I'd heard Granddaddy tell that story a hundred times.

"Naw," said Cheever. "It happened right down there along that big bottom." Cheever pointed through the trees towards the bottomland by Mossy Creek.

"I'd love to hear about that," said Mr. John.

"Aw-right, I'll tell ya," Cheever said, getting up from the log. "But we best be gettin' towards the barn before this boy has a hissy fit."

Thank goodness! I stood up real quick before they could change their minds.

Mr. John closed his book. "Does it make any difference if I leave this book here till we come back?"

"Not to me, it don't," said Cheever.

Mr. John put the book on the log and picked up an old brick to lay on top of it. Then he walked fast to catch up with me and Cheever.

As we walked along, Cheever told the story of the saddle. "While they was fightin' over Atlanta, Sherman sent some of his boys up this way. He claimed it was to protect the pro-Union folks here in the mountain counties. They just came to plunder, though."

"I've heard about that," said Mr. John. "I think that happened in a lot of places up this way."

"Anyhow," Cheever said. "Some of his boys camped along the creek down there." Cheever pointed towards Mossy Creek, even though you couldn't see it from where we were.

"Pa and one of the Dorsey boys—I can't 'call which one now—snuck down there one night and stole a saddle. 'Course, Pa always claimed they 'appropriated' it."

"Either way, that must have been dangerous," said Mr. John.

"I reckon it was," said Cheever. "Pa always said if they'd caught 'em they'd a'hung 'em. But they didn't catch 'em, and Pa rode his ole mule with that saddle on it till it was plum wore out. The mule, too."

Mr. John laughed. "I suppose that saddle was his war trophy. What happened to it?"

"That ole saddle is still yet over there in Pa's house," said Cheever, pointing towards the old house across the road from the shop. "What's left of it, anyhow."

"It's remarkable you still have it," said Mr. John. "Especially with it having such a splendid provenance behind it."

Cheever rubbed his face. "Naw. It didn't have one of them. Just stirrups and a place to sit."

He winked at me.

"Q said that when Pa was a boy, he'd stole that saddle from a private. When he got grown, he'd stole it from a captain. In his middle years, he'd stole it from a colonel. Q always said if Pa had lived to be a hundred, he'd-a stole that saddle from General Sherman his-self!"

Mr. John laughed. "Well, we do tend to exaggerate as we age," he said.

Cheever looked thoughtful again. "I wish I'd asked Pa more about that. But it's too late now. He did tell me that when folks heard the Yankees was comin', they hid their cows and such back in the woods yonder." He pointed towards our house across the creek.

"Did that work?"

"For a while. After them soldiers called in the dogs and peed on the fire, ever'body brought their livestock home. But them blue-bellies had a trick up their sleeves."

"What kind of trick?"

"They came back a day or two later and took ever'thing—even the chickens. Pa said that next winter was the worst he ever spent."

"That was a terrible time all right," said Mr. John. He didn't say anything else for a minute. Then he asked Cheever, "What about your two uncles who made it back home?"

"That was Barney and David. Uncle Barney moved to Dahlonega pretty quick after the war. As for Uncle David, Pa said he came back addled from the fightin'."

Cheever pointed towards Mossy Creek again. "He'd sit on his porch down below the church and shoot at Yankees. 'Course, nobody could see 'em but him."

"That sounds dangerous."

"It was," said Cheever. "Ever' body learned pretty quick to come up the back way if they's any shootin' going on at his house."

"Do you remember him?"

"Naw. Uncle David died six years before I's born. He was just thirty-six years old."

I wasn't listening much anymore. I could smell pigs. Cheever's hog pen was on the far side of the barn.

We were almost there.

CHAPTER FOUR

Cheever's Mule

The old barn finally came in sight.

Me and Lonzo started to run on ahead, but Cheever held up his hand. "Hold on, Embo," he said. "Stand here a minute." Cheever cupped his hand to his ear.

Mr. John did the same thing. He seemed to wonder what we were supposed to be listening for, though.

Lonzo cocked his head and listened with us. I didn't hear anything for a minute except for his panting, and another June bug buzzing by.

Then I heard it. Bang! Then a door rattled. It was coming from the barn.

Cheever grinned and motioned for us to stay still. "He'll do it again in a minute."

There was another bang, followed by one more.

Cheever was tickled. "You hear that?" he asked Mr. John.

"I do. What on earth is it?"

Cheever used his pipe to point towards the barn. "That's ole Jason tellin' us to hurry up."

Mr. John looked confused.

"Ya see," said Cheever, almost proudly. "Whenever that mule hears me comin', he turns his rear end to the door and kicks at it with his hind leg. He's tellin' me it's time we got to work."

Jason was still kicking the door when we got to the corn crib above the barn. I was in a hurry, but Cheever stopped to open the door. He took out two ears from the big pile inside. "I'm comin', ole son," Cheever hollered to Jason. "Hold on while I shuck you an ear of corn."

"If you want, boy," he said to me, "you can run on down and unlatch the stable door. Maybe if you do, he'll quit kicking it. Don't let him out, though."

I ran to the barn as fast as I could with Lonzo running beside me. Then I put my hand on the wooden latch that kept the stable door closed, as Lonzo sat down to help me keep Jason in. When the ole mule turned around and lowered his head, we could see his big face through the wide cracks in the wood.

I pulled the door open to peek in. Jason blew warm air at me through his nostrils. His gray nose felt like the velvet cloth Mother used to make a dress for a woman in Cleveland one time. Lonzo stood up and sniffed at Jason. I heard Mr. John's camera click.

Cheever soon came down the path, shelling kernels from the end of the shucked ear with his thumbs. He dropped them on the ground for the hen who had a nest in the barn.

The fat hen, followed by seven little yellow chicks, ran

out and pecked at the corn like she was starving. The chicks chirped around her while she ate.

Jason nudged me with his nose before turning his head to look at Cheever. The big black barn cat came out of nowhere and rubbed against my leg. When Lonzo barked at him, he climbed up the loft ladder like he had something important to do up there.

Cheever tossed the ear of corn into the feedbox nailed to the wall of Jason's stall. "There ya go, old son," he said. "Eat 'til you bust." Then he rubbed his hand across the mule's back to feel for sores.

Jason made a lot of noise as he crunched the kernels off the cob with his teeth.

"Don't mind him," Cheever said. "When it comes to eatin' corn, ole Jason ain't got the manners of a Billy goat."

Mr. John grinned and watched Cheever take down the collar from its hanger on the wall. After Cheever unbuckled the top, he carried it through the stable door and slipped the horse collar up over the mule's neck. Jason didn't mind. He kept eating.

"Mules are good creatures," said Cheever, patting Jason's neck. "You treat 'em good, give 'em somethin' to eat, you got a friend for life."

"What was it William Faulkner said about mules?" Mr. John then answered his own question. "A mule will labor ten years willingly and patiently, just for the privilege of kicking you really hard one time."

Cheever chuckled. "Well, I never met Will Faulkner," he said, leading Jason from the stable by holding his hand under the mule's chin. "But it sounds to me like he knows a thing or two about mules."

Jason lowered his head to let Cheever slip the bridle on. "That's a good boy," Cheever said, putting his thumb in the corner of Jason's mouth to make him take the bit. "Open up now. That's the way. Good job."

Once the bridle was in place, Jason bobbed his head up and down like it felt good to have it on again.

Cheever walked around the mule, picking up his feet one at a time to look at their bottoms. "I knew a feller one time, had a mule kick his mother-in-law smack dab in the head," he said.

Mr. John seemed concerned. "Did it hurt her much?" he asked.

"Killed her graveyard-dead," said Cheever. "Next day, two hundred men showed up for her funeral."

"She was that well known?"

"Naw," said Cheever. "Word got out, and they was all wantin' to buy that mule."

Mr. John smiled and shook his head. Then he took a picture of Cheever fastening the hames around Jason's collar. Those hames made good handles to hold on to when I rode Jason. I still wanted to do that. It was just that Jason was taller than I remembered.

Once Cheever had everything in place, he stood back to look things over. He adjusted a strap or two here and there and looked down at me. "I'm gonna need you to help me here, Embo."

"How?" I asked.

"Well," he said, tapping tobacco into his pipe. "I want somebody to sit on this mule's back and make sure ever'thing's in good working order. I know your mama said for you not to ride him, but she won't care if you're helpin' me out, will she?"

I grinned and shook my head no. Cheever lit his pipe and dropped the match on the ground. Then he put the pipe in his mouth and swung me up on Jason's back.

I didn't remember it being this far to the ground, so I held the hames tight. Cheever took hold of the bridle and looked at me. "You aw-right, boy?"

I swallowed hard and nodded. Mr. John took another picture, and we started up the trail towards the shop. Lonzo trotted in front like he was showing us the way.

The sweet smell of Cheever's pipe drifted up between the mule's ears. I began feeling a little like Roy Rogers again. But I was pretty sure Trigger wasn't this tall.

As we walked along, Mr. John started asking about the Meaders family again. "You mentioned that one of your uncles who lived through the war moved to Dahlonega. What can you tell me about him?"

"That was Uncle Barney," said Cheever. "Meaders Street over there is named for him. He lit out for Dahlonega pretty quick after the war and opened up a store on the square. His bunch prospered. Lots of stories about that crowd."

I'd heard lots of stories about Uncle Barney, so I only half listened.

A squirrel ran along the limb of a big oak tree. Lonzo saw it, too, and perked up his ears. Cheever still had my slingshot in his pocket, or I'd have taken a shot at it.

When I started listening again, Cheever was still talking about his Uncle Barney. "...one-time, he had a man diggin' post holes for him," he said. "The feller turned up a right good-sized nugget and claimed he'd hit a vein."

"What did Barney do?"

Cheever puffed on his pipe. "When the feller showed him that nugget, Barney told him to put it right back in the ground and set a post in that hole. He said, 'Don't tell nobody where you found that—especially my wife. Else folks'll start diggin' up my pasture, and I won't even be able to keep a milk cow!' What about that?"

Mr. John laughed again. "Well, Dahlonega is known for its gold. Maybe your uncle already had more than he needed."

"Maybe," said Cheever. "Barney and them always had more jingle in their pockets that we did."

"Maybe so," said Mr. John. "But I think you could say that you and your brothers turned the clay you found over here into gold."

Cheever rubbed his chin. "Hadn't thought of it that way. I reckon you're right, though. Even during the Depression, folks managed to scrape up a nickel or two to buy a churn or what not. Had to, to put up what they grew; else they wouldn't have it to eat come winter. Yet it'd be a stretch to call this place a gold mine."

"I suppose so," agreed Mr. John.

Cheever looked back at me. "Ever' thing aw-right, boy?"

I nodded that it was.

"I reckon we fared better'n most," said Cheever. "Pa did a good thing startin' that ware shop up."

"What was your father like?" asked Mr. John.

"Well," said Cheever. "Pa could be right hard sometimes, but he was the strongest man I ever saw. He could lift a loaded wagon if he had a mind to."

Then he chuckled to himself. "He likely wouldn't a helped load it, though."

I was busy taking a one-fingered aim at some cow-stealing Yankee on the trail ahead when I saw something that made me lower my hand-gun. There sat Arie and Miss Nancy on the same log we'd sat on earlier.

Cheever saw them too, and hollered, "What y'all mean loaferin' around that-a-way? Why I'd a-thought you two would have a kiln of pott'ry ready for me to fire by now."

Arie looked at me, then at Cheever. "You know what

that boy's mama said about him being on that mule," she said.

Cheever turned around and looked surprised to see me on Jason. "Good Lord, son!" he said. "How'd you get up there without me knowin' it?"

He walked over to me and reached up. "Here, let me get you down from there, Embo. I declare, I gotta watch you ever' minute." Then he winked at me again.

"You're the one that needs watching," said Arie, as Cheever pulled me off Jason's back. I would have begged to stay up there a few minutes more, but I knew better.

Besides, I'd already spotted the wax-paper-covered plate of teacakes Arie had in her lap.

CHAPTER FIVE

Cheever's Log

Cheever tied the bridle's reins to a small tree and tapped his pipe against the tree trunk to empty the bowl.

Mr. John walked over to the log. When Miss Nancy patted her hand on it, he sat down beside her. "Were y'all looking for us?" he asked.

"We woulda been before long," said Arie. "It don't generally take Cheever an hour to fetch a mule. But no—we went to the house to get these teacakes and somethin' cold to drink."

She pulled back the wax-paper. "Y'all want one?"

I did. So did Lonzo, but Arie shooed him off when he sniffed at them. Everybody took a teacake except Miss Nancy. I took the one with the most powdered sugar on top.

Those were the best. Then Arie wrapped the wax-paper back over the plate.

Cheever tossed Lonzo a piece of his. I meant to give him some of mine, too, but he ran off before I could.

Cheever grunted as he sat down on the log beside Arie. She reached under the wax-paper, got out another teacake and handed it to him. He took it and gave it to me.

"Don't spoil his dinner," Arie said.

"That little bite won't hurt none," he said. Then he reached into his pocket and took out the Prince Albert can.

Miss Nancy had that big book we'd left on the log in her lap. "I *was* beginning to get a little worried," she said. "Did you mean to leave this book here?"

"Yes," said Mr. John. "I got it from the car to look up something. We were in a hurry, so I left it there. Then we got to talking. You know how that goes."

"I do," she said, laughing. "What all did you talk about? Oh, let me guess. I bet it had something to do with history."

"In a way," said Mr. John, taking a bite of his teacake. "These are wonderful," he said to Arie. "You really ought to try one, Nancy."

"All right," she said, looking at the plate. "You've talked me into it."

Arie pulled back the wax-paper, and Miss Nancy took the smallest teacake on the plate.

Mr. John finished the rest of his and said, "We've mostly been talking about the Meaders family—and mules." He brushed his hand across his pants to wipe off some powdered sugar. "Most recently about Mr. Cheever's father. We were trying to figure out his role in the Civil War."

"Did you tell him about your pa's war pension?" Arie asked Cheever.

Mr. John looked surprised. "He had a war pension?"

"Sorta," said Cheever, lighting his pipe. "At least he thought he did."

"How so?" asked Mr. John.

Cheever blew out a big puff of smoke. "Ya see, when they first got up Social Security, Pa thought it was welfare. And he didn't want no part of it. But Camilla and them needed that money somethin' awful."

While Cheever was talking, Arie unscrewed the lid from the glass jug of water she'd brought from the house. Its outside was wet. She emptied some into the dipper that usually hung by their well and handed it to me.

"Here, Emory," she said. "You need to drink some water."

I did. It had ice cubes in it, so it was still tooth-cracking cold, as Granddaddy would say. I tossed the last bit of water into the woods and handed the dipper back to Arie.

"Anybody else want a drink?" Arie asked. Nobody did, so she screwed the lid back on the jug and put it on the ground with the dipper.

"So, what happened with that war pension?" Miss Nancy asked. "I'm curious."

"Camilla outsmarted him," said Arie. "That's what happened."

Miss Nancy leaned forward to look at Arie. "How did she do that?"

"Camilla told him the government had come up with a new pension plan for Confederate veterans."

"And that was all right with him?" asked Mr. John.

"It was," said Cheever. "He thought he'd earned that."

"For stealing that saddle, I reckon," said Arie.

Miss Nancy looked confused. "What saddle?"

Mr. John grinned at her. "I'll fill you in later," he said.

Cheever kept going with his story. "Camilla never did let Pa see any of them checks. She cashed 'em up in Cleveland, and they got twelve dollars a month from 1940 'till he died in forty-three."

"That was clever of Camilla," said Mr. John. Then he looked at Arie and said, "Mrs. Meaders, I bet you have quite a few stories to tell as well."

Arie blew at a gnat buzzing around her face. "None that I know of," she said.

"Tell 'em about meetin' the President," said Cheever. "He'll like that story."

"Why don't you tell about your cousin Bob meetin' him," said Arie. "He'll like that better."

Cheever seemed to agree. "That *is* a good story. And *that* one really happened. You want to hear it?"

"Certainly," said Mr. John. "Remind me again, who Bob is, and which President we're talking about."

"Roosevelt," said Cheever, like Mr. John should have known that. "Bob was one of Uncle Barney's boys over in Dahlonega. He always did have a head-full of sense."

I was bored, so I walked over to Jason and petted his face. Lonzo came, too. He wanted me to throw a stick, but I said, "Not now, Lonzo. I gotta watch this mule. Me and you'll play later."

Lonzo looked disappointed, but when he went back to the log, Cheever rubbed his ears.

"And your cousin Bob really did meet the President?" asked Miss Nancy.

"He did," said Cheever. "Ya see, back when Roosevelt first run, they got up a big rally for him down in Atlanta. Bob was a supporter, so he went down for it. When it come time to shake hands, Bob grabbed Roosevelt's tie and, real quick like, pinned one of them Dahlonega-nugget stick-pins to it."

"My gracious," said Mr. John. "I'm surprised the Secret Service let that happen."

Cheever laughed. "Well, things waddn't as strict back then. Plus, he waddn't the President yet."

Arie looked like she didn't agree. "Why, two of 'em wrestled Bob to the ground before he could see straight," she said.

Cheever chuckled. "Yeah," he said. "I reckon they did. But Roosevelt wore that pin for the rest of the day, so Bob thought it was worth it. Plus, it got wrote up in the papers."

Miss Nancy leaned forward again to see Arie better. "Well, Mrs. Meaders, we've heard Bob's story about meeting the President. I'm sure John would really like to hear yours. So would I."

"He'll laugh," said Arie.

"I won't. I promise," said Mr. John.

Arie frowned. "I was talking about Cheever."

"Oh," said Mr. John, looking embarrassed.

Cheever stretched out his legs. "I'll turn the other way if I can't help laughing," he said to Arie. "Anyhow, sellin' pott'ry to the President is something to brag about."

"Well, it's the truth," said Arie. "Even if nobody does believe me."

"This sounds interesting," said Miss Nancy.

Arie sighed. "Well, all right then," she said. "I'll tell it. It was in the spring of 1938. I was down there at the house, in the front room, feeding our baby, Ruby. She was just three or four months old then.

"A big ole car pulled off the road, and the ugliest woman I'd ever seen got out of it. The front door was standing open, but she knocked on it anyway."

"My goodness," said Miss Nancy. "What did she want?"

Arie looked over at Cheever before she answered. He wasn't laughing or anything, so she kept talking. "She pointed to a little clay pot sittin' on the rail and said she wanted to buy it. She talked so twangy, I barely could make out what she was sayin'."

"That's fascinating," said Miss Nancy. "What happened next?"

"I told her I was usin' that little pot and didn't want to sell it. That we had plenty more like it up there at the shop. 'Course that wouldn't do a-tall! She said her husband had seen that one from the road and wanted it."

"Then what happened?" asked Miss Nancy.

"I sold it to her. Told her I'd take a dime for it, but that she could get one like it up here for a nickel."

"Was that all there was to it?" asked Mr. John.

"About. She gave me a dime, and I handed her the pot."

"Did she say anything else?" asked Miss Nancy.

She sure was interested in this.

"Well, she mentioned my jonquils—they'd bloomed early that year. I said her hat suited her. It didn't really. I couldn't come up with much else to say, so she left."

Arie's voice went higher. "When they drove off, the man turned around to wave, and it was President Franklin Delano Roosevelt! And that woman was Eleanor—The First Lady! I know it."

Arie looked at Cheever again. He didn't say a word. He just pulled a tick out of Lonzo's ear and flipped it into the woods.

"Do you think it really was the Roosevelts?" asked Mr. John.

"I wouldn't a-told it if I didn't." Arie pointed at Cheever with her thumb. "He don't believe it though—never has."

Mr. John looked at Cheever. "So, you aren't convinced that was really the Roosevelts?"

Cheever studied for a moment. "Oh, I reckon I am now. After what happened last week."

"What happened last week?"

"Lyndon Johnson stopped by."

Arie didn't think that was funny, but I could tell Mr. John was enjoying the story.

"Did he, now?" he asked.

"Yeah," said Cheever. "He bought some churns and a pitcher for Lady Bird. Said he's gettin' her a cow before long. She's gonna start churnin' her own butter at the White House."

Miss Nancy laughed, but Mr. John turned serious again. "You know, it could be true," he said, rubbing his chin.

"Sure it is," said Cheever. "Lots of the First Ladies churned their own butter."

"No. I mean about FDR stopping by—not Johnson."

Cheever pretended that hurt his feelings. "You mean you'll believe Arie's story and not mine? That beats a hen a'rootin'."

"Mine's the truth," said Arie, looking mad again.

"Well, if it was Roosevelt," said Cheever, "why didn't he ask you to vote for him? Don't sound like a politician to me."

"Why would he?" asked Arie.

Mr. John looked around to see what Cheever would say.

When he didn't say anything, Mr. John did. "Neither man would have likely felt the need to campaign much in Georgia. He was deep in Dixie—Democrat land."

"Yeah," said Cheever. "Don't reckon I ever even met a Republican—you ain't one, are you?"

Mr. John didn't answer. I wondered if you could tell a Republican from a Democrat by looking. Maybe they had a secret handshake or something.

Mr. John looked at Arie and tilted his head a little. "Mrs. Meaders, did you say this visit happened in 1938?"

"I did. In the spring."

"That's amazing," he said.

"What is?" Arie asked.

"Your story. You see, Nancy and I stopped in Gainesville the other day. I'd forgotten this until I read the marker, but the town square down there is named for FDR."

"I didn't know that," Arie admitted.

"Well it is," said Mr. John. "That's because Roosevelt was instrumental in rebuilding Gainesville after that tornado destroyed the town in 1936. He saw the destruction first-hand and was moved. So, he came back in March of 1938 to dedicate everything that had been rebuilt."

"That don't prove nothin'," said Cheever.

Mr. John was excited. "Don't you see, Mr. Meaders? It puts the president within twenty miles of here at the time your wife claims to have seen him. That's amazing!"

Cheever wasn't amazed. "Humph," he said. "Even if he did come to Gainesville, the Secret Service wouldn't let 'em come traipsing off up here."

Mr. John was thinking in his head again. "I've read that Roosevelt would sometimes elude his guards when he visited his retreat at Warm Springs. Maybe that's what he did in Gainesville."

"Maybe he came up here to check on the electricity," said Arie.

Mr. John looked at her. "You know, Mrs. Meaders, you may be right."

"Or maybe he was bringin' cousin Bob's tie-pin back," said Cheever.

That made Miss Nancy smile.

Mr. John was still thinking. "That *was* about the time the Rural Electrification Administration was getting underway. You, know—the REA?"

"Oh, we know the REA all right," said Arie. "Country folks speak of the Bible and the REA in the same tone of reverence."

Mr. John nodded. "I know what you mean. Do you remember when you first got electricity?"

"The very day!" said Arie. "And some folks didn't want it! Thought electricity would burn the house down. But I was tickled to death to get it."

"I know what you mean," said Mr. John. "There was some resistance to electricity at first, especially among the older folks. I remember an advertising campaign called 'Kick the Lamp.' It had a drawing of a little man in his nightgown kicking over a kerosene lamp."

Cheever looked at him funny. "Why would they want anybody to kick over a kerosene lamp? That's liable to catch somebody's house a'fire."

Mr. John cleared his throat. "The idea was to encourage people to use electric lights instead of kerosene lamps."

"Well, that waddn't no way to do it," said Cheever. "Tellin' folks to kick over a lamp; I never heard of such."

Mr. John didn't say anything for a minute. Then he changed the subject.

"They wired my grandmother's house in 1939," he said. "I was just ten. She let them put electricity on the first floor, but not on the second."

"Not upstairs?" asked Arie. "Why not?"

Miss Nancy answered instead of him. "John's grandmother said it was too close to the lightning, and God would strike the whole family down if they put electricity up there."

I wondered why God would do something like that over electricity. Surely, they had electricity in Heaven.

Mr. John laughed again. "We've honored her wishes. The second floor is still electricity free. And that's where all the bedrooms are."

"Well then," said Cheever, "It musta worked."

"What worked?"

"Keeping God from strikin' ever' thing down and destroyin' it all. It is still standin', ain't it?"

Mr. John laughed. "It is," he admitted. "I hadn't thought about it that way." Then he added, "I imagine electricity made producing pottery quite a bit easier, didn't it, Mr. Meaders?"

"How would it?" Cheever asked him back.

Arie started talking again before Mr. John could answer. "About all Cheever did up at the shop was put in a light bulb—at least for a long time. It's wired up a little better now."

"Well, they didn't *give* electricity away," said Cheever. "You had to pay for it—still do."

Arie didn't pay Cheever any attention. "Our boy, Lanier, feels different. And he's smart as a whip when it comes to things like that. He's been wantin' ta cobble up some sort of electric pugmill, but Cheever won't hear-tell of it."

"I would think an electric-powered machine would offer advantages over the older way of mixing clay, wouldn't it, Mr. Meaders?" asked Mr. John.

"It takes a mule to mix up clay right," said Cheever. "Why, an electrified pugmill wouldn't be good for nothin' but noise."

Good. "It's all right boy," I whispered to Jason. "Your job's safe." When I stroked his neck, he tossed his head like he understood.

Arie was still thinking about when the electricity came. "The biggest thing about gettin' electricity was havin' running water at the house," she said.

I'd heard Grandmother say the same thing.

"I've never lived without electricity," said Miss Nancy. "I can't imagine it."

"Aw," said Cheever, blowing pipe smoke. "We always had running water."

Mr. John looked surprised. "You did?" he said.

"Yeah," said Cheever. "We'd *run* to the well, pull up a bucketful and *run* back to the house with it."

"I'm not sure that qualifies," said Mr. John, smiling.

"I never did like pipe water," said Cheever. "Water that's been sittin' in them ole iron pipes all day. No tellin' what all's in it. Good water comes right outta the ground, the way God intended."

"There's probably truth to that," said Mr. John.

"There is," said Cheever. "That's why I never let 'em run it up here. That ole rain barrel is all we ever needed." Cheever pointed towards the shop with his pipe.

"Well, I have heard some good things about spring water," said Miss Nancy.

Cheever scratched Lonzo's ears again. "Spring water saved one of Wiley's boy's life a few years back." Then he pointed at me. "Wiley's Embo's granddaddy."

That was the truth about Uncle Crick. I don't think Mr. John believed it, though, because he stopped writing.

"Really?" he asked. "How so?"

"Wiley's oldest boy—his name's Christopher, but everybody calls him Crick—anyway, his appendix ruptured. It got so bad they'd put him in the back room of that hospital down at Gainesville."

"The back room?" asked Mr. John, like he'd never heard of a hospital having a back room.

"Yeah," said Cheever. "That's where they put the ones they expect ta die pretty quick. Crick was burning up with fever. But he told Wiley if he could get one drink of that good spring water from back home, he'd be all right."

"Was your brother able to get it for him?" Mr. John asked.

"He hitched a ride home and came back with a jug full," said Cheever. "The folks at the hospital thought it was whiskey and wouldn't let him in with it."

"Really? What did he do?"

"Why, they waddn't enough doctors in that hospital to keep Wiley from gettin' that water to his boy. He marched into that room and blocked the door till Crick drank all of it he wanted. A day or two later, that boy came home fit as a fiddle."

That was why Uncle Crick went to the spring to get a gallon of water when he came to visit on Sundays.

Arie wasn't paying attention to the Crick story. "When we got the electricity," she said, "we just had one little bulb danglin' from the ceiling in the kitchen. But it was wonderful. 'Course we never had a bathroom. Least till I got to where I could pay for it."

"Why not?" asked Miss Nancy.

Arie pointed to Cheever. "Because of him."

Cheever shook his head. "The old outhouse suited fine. Besides, a person ain't meant to take a..."

He was about to say a bad word, so Arie hushed him.

"Let me say it this way," he said. "The Good Lord never intended for us to use the bathroom and take our meals under the same roof—ain't right."

Mr. John and Miss Nancy smiled at each other.

"I guess we'll have to agree to disagree on that, Mr. Meaders," said Mr. John. Then he turned to Arie. "Mrs. Meaders, when did you finally get that bathroom?"

"Once I started makin' a little side-money last year, I saved up for it. Puttin' in that bathroom was the best thing I ever did."

"Pshaw," said Cheever.

Mr. John looked at him. "You don't agree with her about that, Mr. Meaders?"

"Maybe a little," he admitted. "But I still yet keep a chamber pot close." Then he chuckled and looked towards his house. "But I reckon that room does come in handy—on cold nights, anyhow."

Everybody laughed when he said that.

"I noticed you have a radio now," Mr. John said to Arie. "I bet you acquired one of those pretty soon after you got electricity, didn't you?"

"Why, we didn't get one of them 'til after Pearl Harbor," she said. Then she looked over at Cheever. "That was because of him, too."

If Cheever heard her, he didn't say anything.

"Pearl Harbor?" John asked. "I don't understand."

Cheever certainly heard that, because he said, "Well, you surprise me, Painter Man. What with you bein' so interested in history and all. It was in all the papers."

Mr. John rubbed his hand over his face. Then he looked at Miss Nancy. "Well, I do know about Pearl Harbor. Not as well as Nancy does, though. You see, she was there when Japan attacked."

"Goodness gracious," said Arie, looking surprised.

Everybody looked at Miss Nancy. "Let's not talk about that," she said. "Anyway, I was in Honolulu, not on the base itself. My daddy was stationed there, you see."

Arie stared at Miss Nancy, "Well, I declare. While we was over here gettin' the news piecemeal, you already knew ever' thing firsthand."

"Oh, I was just little," said Miss Nancy, "so I didn't really know what was happening—not the big picture, anyway. Right after the attack was over, Daddy sent my brother and me back to live with our uncle in Virginia. Mother, too."

"My goodness," said Arie. "I ain't hardly been nowhere a'tall."

I had. I'd been all the way to Florida. I started to tell Miss Nancy that, but they all seemed too busy to notice me. I patted Jason's nose one last time and went over to the log. I hoped Arie would offer me another teacake, but she didn't.

Miss Nancy touched Arie's arm. "Tell us more about the radio."

That seemed to suit Arie. "Well," she said. "Ole man Alf Stover had the first one around here. It was a great big ole thing. And ever' Saturday night, ever' body who could walk went over to his house. He'd roll that radio out on the porch, and we'd listen to the Grand Old Opry. 'Course Cheever hardly ever went."

"I never had time," he said. "Unless Roy Acuff was singin'. Besides, I could make my own music."

"Oh?" said Mr. John, looking interested. "What do you play?"

"A little on the mandolin. The French harp, too. How 'bout I play *Yankee Doodle Dandy* for ya while we walk on down to the shop?"

He tapped his pipe against the log to knock out the ashes and slipped it into his pocket. Then he stood up and pulled out his French harp.

"Sounds good to me," said Mr. John. He picked up his book and stood, too. Then he reached his hand out to Miss Nancy, who took it to pull up.

Arie stood all by herself and got the water jug and dipper. Miss Nancy picked up the plate of teacakes.

Once everybody was ready, Cheever motioned towards the shop.

"Y'all go on ahead," he said. "Nobody needs to walk behind a mule when it ain't necessary."

CHAPTER SIX

Cheever's Recollections

When they started towards the shop, Cheever put his finger to his lips to shush me. Then, quick as a flash, he swung me up on Jason's back and handed me the reins.

Once we headed towards the shop, too, Cheever started playing *Yankee Doodle Dandy* with both hands on the harp. Jason didn't need to be guided because he followed Cheever without me even saying giddy-up.

Miss Nancy stepped in time to the tune. She sang along, too. Mr. John clapped his hand against his big book, but he didn't sing.

The song finished just as we got to the shop. Mr. John

and Miss Nancy put down the things they'd been carrying and clapped some more.

Cheever was getting ready to play another tune, but Arie waved her hand. "Don't encourage him. He won't quit playin' till dark if you do."

"That was wonderful!" said Miss Nancy. "Really! You're very, very good."

"Aw, I used to be," said Cheever, looking down at his French harp. "This ole thing's about wore out." He pushed the instrument back in his pocket. "Sorta like me, I reckon."

Miss Nancy touched his arm. "Not at all," she said, in a kind voice.

Cheever looked like he didn't know what to say. He just nodded. Then he reached up to help me off Jason's back. "We'll grind that clay after while, Embo," he said, real quiet-like. "I got things ta do in the shop first."

He led Jason to a shady spot by the kiln, tied the reins to one of the posts that held up the tin and dipped a bucket of water from the rain barrel for the mule. Lonzo lay down in the shade of the mule's belly and watched us go back in the shop.

Cheever picked up another old foot-tub and dipped it in the rain barrel to get some more water for inside the shop.

Arie put her apron back on and sat down. When she patted the chair beside her, Miss Nancy sat down, too.

I took my shoes and socks back off.

When I went over to my vase, the daisies had been smoothed over again. Miss Nancy smiled at me, and I felt a little better after that.

Arie saw me looking. "They were good, Emory, but I know you can do even better. Make the stems longer this time."

I didn't think I could do better. But I sat back down and started over again. I think Miss Nancy felt sorry for me.

Mr. John put his camera in his bag and took out his

notebook. "Mrs. Meaders," he said, "a while ago, you mentioned buying a radio shortly after Pearl Harbor. Can you tell us the rest of that story?"

"Well," said Arie, "a radio got to be something we needed to keep up with the war news."

"I see," said Mr. John, sitting in his chair again so he could write that down.

Cheever put the bucket of water on the floor and took his pipe out of his pocket. "With a radio, you can hear about something nearly as quick as it happens," he said. "Plus, they play music sometimes."

Arie pinched off some clay from the ball and started rolling another grape. "The Sunday Pearl Harbor happened, two of Wiley's boys, Ray and Crick, came over here to tell us about it."

"I remember that," said Cheever, dipping a jar into the bucket of water. He poured water onto the wheel and started it turning. "Them and our boys kept running back and forth to Alf Stover's to tell ever' body the news."

Arie quit rolling the clay in her hand. "The numbers kept going up and up," she said.

I wondered what numbers she meant. Then everybody stayed quiet for a minute.

Arie was the first to speak again. "That was a bad day." Then she rolled another grape.

"Did all four of your boys serve in the military?" Mr. John asked, as Cheever looked around for his wood chip.

When he found it, he said, "All of 'em went across the pond but Edwin. He's the youngest."

"Our boys did their part," said Arie. Then she seemed sad again. "But Lanier came home different."

Miss Nancy put her hand on Arie's arm. "Different?" she asked. "Different how?"

"For one thing, he was quieter," said Arie. "Before the war, he was the life of the party. He was the one they'd always pick for the lead in the Christmas play at church."

"Yeah," said Cheever. He pressed the wood chip's flat edge against the wheel to clean the surface as it turned. "And he always sang a solo song, too. But he didn't sing much after the war."

Mr. John changed the subject again. "I'm still fascinated by the possibility of President Roosevelt visiting here. That tornado damage must have really caught his attention. Do you remember much about that?"

"Law, yes!" said Arie. "It was awful—killed so many people. I never will forget how dark it got that morning. You remember that, Cheever?"

"Sure do," he said, washing his chip off in the bucket. "Pa happened to be over here that morning, and we went out in the yard to look."

Cheever walked to the door. Then he pointed towards the sky. "Way off up yonder in the clouds was this green door," he said. "It was just a-floatin' and a-turnin' as pretty as you please; slow motion like. Pa and me watched that door for a good long while."

"A door?"

"Yeah," said Cheever. "After it was gone, Pa studied a minute and said, 'a tornado's hit Gainesville.' He seemed right sure about that, too."

"How did he know?"

"That's what I asked him. 'Well,' he says, 'Gainesville's the closest place around that's got painted doors.'"

"That's amazing. Did that tornado do much damage up this way?"

"Not much," said Cheever. "It knocked down a few trees and what-not. That just meant more wood for the kiln."

Arie looked at Miss Nancy and said, "I heard tell of a letter from Gainesville blowin' clear to South Carolina from that storm. What about that?"

Before Miss Nancy could answer, Cheever said, "That ain't nothin'. I heard tell of a package from the Gainesville post office flyin' all the way to Virginia."

"Really?" asked Miss Nancy. "From that storm?"

Cheever grinned. "Naw. Some feller'd mailed it a day or two before."

Everybody laughed except Arie. I think she'd heard that story before.

"This is fascinating," Mr. John said to Cheever. "But let's get back to you and your family, Mr. Meaders. And I'd like to hear more about pottery."

Cheever wiped his hands off. Then he tapped more tobacco into his pipe. "Aw-right," he said. "But pott'ry ain't nothin' but mud and hard work with a little sweat thrown in ta boot. What more ya wanna know?"

Mr. John looked around the room. "How about if we begin here? How did this shop get started?"

"Well," said Cheever, lighting his pipe. "Pa started all this up in the winter of eighteen-hundred and ninety-two. They was lots of potters around then. They sold ever'thing they could make and then some."

"I see," said Mr. John, writing fast.

Cheever waited a minute to let him write. "Pa looked around and saw the Dorseys and Pitchfords, the Hewells and ever' body making money at it...and there was a real need for what they made. So, Pa thought he'd just put him up a ware shop, too."

He turned to look outside again. "Pa had boys that could work. The problem was, none of us could turn."

"How did he fix that?"

"He hired a feller to teach my older brothers. After a year or two, they got pretty good at it. Then they taught the rest of us. I's just five or six then—never knew nothing else."

"Did he teach your father how to turn, too?"

"Naw," said Cheever. "Pa left turning to us boys. He was a waggoneer. He'd go all over creation haulin' anything he could sell. He even hauled pott'ry for the Dorseys before we started makin' it ourselves."

"Did the Dorseys not haul their own pottery?"

"Aw, we all helped one another. Daddy Bill Dorsey was like Pa. He didn't turn, but his boys did. He married one of Pa's sisters, so we was sorta kin to him that way."

Arie thought of something funny and chuckled. "Cheever, tell him about Daddy Bill gettin' the hiccups."

"What'd you say?" he asked.

"Nothing," said Arie, shaking her head.

"Good. 'Cause I's fixin' to tell about Daddy Bill gettin' the hiccups."

"The hiccups?" asked Mr. John.

"He had 'em bad," said Cheever. "Couldn't sleep for three weeks. Tried ever'thing to cure 'em. Even had his boys hold him down and tickle him."

"Did that work?"

"Naw. Then somebody told him ammonia would cure 'em, so he spent a night in the outhouse."

"Really? The outhouse? Did that work?"

Arie and Miss Nancy both laughed.

Cheever thought the question was funny, too. "Sleepin' in a outhouse won't cure much a'nothin'."

"I imagine not," said Mr. John. "Did he eventually find a remedy?"

"Naw," said Cheever. "They just stopped real sudden like. But after that, Daddy Bill's mind was gone."

Mr. John stopped writing again. "His mind was gone? From the hiccups?"

"More likely from spendin' the night in an outhouse," said Arie, nudging Miss Nancy with her elbow.

"Whatever it was," said Cheever, "from then on, he was loony as a Bessie bug."

"That's the truth," said Arie. "Before them hiccups came on him, he was the smartest feller around. Except for being forgetful."

"Forgetful?" asked Miss Nancy.

"Yeah," said Arie. "After Daddy Bill got up in years, he'd take off somewhere with a load of ware. When he'd make camp that night, they'd always be somethin' or other he forgot. He found a way around it, though."

"What did he do?" Miss Nancy asked.

"Well," said Arie. "He got to where he'd load up the wagon and drive off a little ways. Then he'd make camp in sight of his house. Come mornin', he'd know what he's missing, and walk back home and get it."

"Did he really do that?" asked Miss Nancy.

"He did," said Cheever. "I thought it was a right good idea myself."

Arie rolled her eyes, but Cheever didn't see her do it. He was already thinking about something else.

"My brother Q took after Pa when it comes to wagoneering," he said. "Q could turn as good as anybody, but he *loved* to sell it. He even got hired by one or two of the schools to teach it for a while."

Mr. John wrote that down. "I've meant to ask," he said. "What do the initials L.Q. stand for?"

"Don't stand for nothin'. That's how Mama wrote it in the Bible. We just called him Q for short."

"Like a nickname. That fits. Where did L.Q. teach pottery?"

"He taught down in South Georgia for a while. Then at that girl college in Gainesville—*Bur-now* they call it. But, Q loved to haul. So, before long, he got to wantin' him a truck. And he got one, too. That was in nineteen hundred and thirty-four."

"No, it waddn't," said Arie, using a rolling pin to flatten clay to make a leaf. "It was nineteen hundred and thirty-five. In May."

Cheever thought for a minute. "Maybe so," he said. "But I remember exactly what he paid for it."

"I doubt it," Arie mumbled.

"What?"

Arie looked at him. "I said I don't doubt it."

Miss Nancy hid her smile again.

"Well, you ought not to," said Cheever. "Q gave the equivalent of one hundred and sixty-one dollars and twenty-cents for that truck."

Mr. John looked up from his writing. "The equivalent?"

"That's right. Money was tight back then. So, folks traded out."

Mr. John tapped his pencil on his notebook. "That was about the time of the Great Depression. Money was scarce everywhere."

"Yeah, it was," said Cheever "But Q scraped up a little over twenty dollars cash and paid the balance in pott'ry. It was eleven hundred, thirty-seven-and-one-half gallons, to be delivered in a month's time."

Mr. John looked like he was counting in his head. "They must have valued the pottery at ten cents a gallon. That's a lot of pottery."

Cheever thought that was funny. "Pshaw. Why an *average* potter could turn fifty gallons a day without tryin' hard—more if they's makin' big pieces. I could turn twice that if I put my mind to it."

"Or, if you didn't spend all day gabbin'," said Arie.

Cheever didn't hear her. Or maybe he chose not to. Granddaddy did that sometimes.

"I helped Q make that truck pott'ry," he said. "That's how come me to remember the exact amount."

"I suppose having a truck made transporting pottery a lot easier," said Mr. John.

Arie laughed. "A'body'd think that, wouldn't they?"

"You don't believe it did, Mrs. Meaders?" Miss Nancy asked.

Cheever answered before she could. "Well, that truck could haul more'n what a wagon could. And instead of taking three or four days to run the route to Murphy, Q could make the trip in two."

"Not that first load," said Arie. "It took him a day to get to Cleveland—that's just four miles."

"Aw," said Cheever. "You ought not tell that."

"Why not? They'll want to hear it."

"What happened?" asked Mr. John.

Arie picked up a clay grape that rolled off the table. "Right after he got that truck, Q and Lanier filled it up with ware—mostly churns and such. They put straw between 'em like they would in a wagon—packed 'em up good and tight. Then they started out across the mountain."

"I take it something went wrong," said Miss Nancy, watching Arie roll a string of clay between her hands to make a vine.

"Why, they had two flat tires before they got outta sight," said Arie, laughing. "That ole truck finally left 'em afoot."

"Well, it was new to 'em then," said Cheever. "And they had the blame thing overloaded. That next day, they made it on to Murphy."

"Not without patchin' up two or three more tires," said Arie.

"I reckon not," admitted Cheever. "After that, they learned not to load the truck so heavy."

"And to dodge holes better," said Arie.

Cheever got asked another question before he could say anything about that.

"I take it you and your brothers had regular distribution routes?"

"We did. Most ever' community had a store. So, there was lots of places to stop before you got to wherever it was you's goin'."

"I see," said Mr. John. "Did you and your brothers transport pottery year-round?"

"We mostly did that in the summer and fall," said Cheever. "We was busy plantin' in the spring, and the roads got too bad in the winter. Plus, I never did like the cold."

"Did you prefer hauling in a wagon or a truck?"

"I never did learn to drive," said Cheever. "Cars go too fast for me."

He watched Mr. John write that down. "Wagons had drawbacks, too, I reckon."

"Like what?"

"Well, some people thought they was slow. But that didn't bother me none. If I was ever in a hurry, it was a slow hurry."

"Any other drawbacks to a wagon?"

Cheever looked like he was thinking. "I knew a feller one time, woke up with his ear froze to the wagon wheel. But that was a rare thing."

Mr. John wrote that down.

"I'll tell ya one thing," said Cheever. "I never had a flat tire on a wagon."

"Tell him about Wiley gettin' stranded on Blood

Mountain," said Arie, lacing a clay vine around a cluster of grapes. "That's a right good tale."

Good. I liked Cheever's stories that had Granddaddy in them.

"That waddn't the wagon's fault," said Cheever.

"It never woulda happened in a truck," Arie said back.

Mr. John turned over a page in his notebook. "That sounds like a story I'd like to hear," he said,

"Well, I'll tell ya then," said Cheever. "It was right after World War One—nineteen hundred and nineteen."

"Last time you told it, it was nineteen and twenty," said Arie.

Mr. John took the peanut Cheever offered him and cracked it open real slow like he was watching a show.

"That might be right," said Cheever. "I know Wiley hadn't been married long, because he was still in a hurry to get back home."

"Cheever!" said Arie, looking across at me and then back at him.

I wondered what I had missed.

"Well, it's the truth," said Cheever. "Anyhow, Wiley had two mules pullin', and he'd make camp in one of them protected zones."

"What's a protected zone?" asked Mr. John, reaching for another peanut.

I was glad he asked, because I wondered that, too.

"Just a spot where a feller could camp in peace," said Cheever. "If you stayed within so many feet of the road, you could burn what firewood you found, and such. Folks would congregate, and Lord, the stories you'd hear."

"And tell," said Arie, without looking up.

Cheever grinned. "I mighta told one or two," he said. "If they begged me."

"And the more they passed that jug around, the taller them tales got," Arie said. "Least that's what I hear."

Cheever looked at me. "You don't have to tell your mama about anybody passin' a jug around," he said. "That might get Wiley in hot water."

"I won't," I said, not wanting Granddaddy to get in hot water. I wondered what kind of jug would make people tell tales.

"Did you like to camp?"

Mr. John's question seemed to get Cheever thinking.

I still see and smell the pipe smoke lingering in the air—Cheever's face concentrated in thought. Not a man who reads or writes much, but a thinking man. He walks over to the door and looks out towards the house he grew up in. It's a view he has been looking at his entire life. As a boy, I see this as nothing special— just part of who Cheever is. As a man, now almost as old as he was then, I wish I could have this time again to ask his thoughts, say the right questions. He turns away from the door, takes out his pipe, studies it.

"Ain't nothin' like bein' out on the road," he said. "Make camp. Fix supper. Play the mouth harp some. Tell some stories. Maybe lay around a while before you go to bed— called it bed. It was just a pallet by the fire. But a man could sleep like he was goin' to the graveyard."

He was quiet for a moment like he was thinking about those days. Then picked up one of the pitchers he'd made a while ago and started towards the back shelf with it.

"Gettin' back to Wiley," he said. "Come daylight, he hitched up his mules. When he slapped the reins, that ole flop-eared mule stepped forward, but the other 'en dropped dead in his tracks."

"My goodness," said Miss Nancy. "What happened to it?"

"Mule measles," said Cheever, winking at me.

"Mule measles?" asked Miss Nancy.

"Either that or mule mumps," said Cheever. "It's hard to tell which on a dark mule."

Arie looked at Miss Nancy and shook her head. "He's pulling your leg, honey. Don't pay him no attention."

She smiled. "Somehow, I suspected that."

Cheever grinned back. "Whatever it was, that mule was dead as a doornail. Wiley had to cut the traces and roll him off down the mountain."

Granddaddy told that story every time we went across the mountain to see Grandmother's people in Murphy. Whenever we got to that place where the mule died, I'd beg Mother to stop and let me look for the bones.

She never did, though.

"Could your brother continue with one mule?" Mr. John asked.

"Naw. Wiley had a big load, and the road was too steep for one mule. He had to twiddle his thumbs a while. Bidin' that much time was right hard on a newlywed."

"Cheever!" Arie hollered.

"Well, it was," he said. "You and me was newlyweds one time, remember?"

"Barely," said Arie.

I wasn't sure why, but my face turned red again.

"So, was Wiley able to finish his trip?"

"Yeah," said Cheever. His pipe had gone out, so he laid it on the wedging table. "He sent word for Cleater to bring him another mule."

Arie reached for more clay. "Tell him about how Wiley got that new mule to replace the one that died."

"Aw-right, I will," said Cheever. "To get a new mule,

Wiley had to hitch a ride to the mule barn in Gainesville. And he had to decide if he was gonna get a young mule or an older one."

"What's the difference?" Miss Nancy asked.

"Money," said Arie, laughing.

Cheever must not have heard her because he repeated what she said.

"It was money. Ya see an older mule, trained to harness and all, always cost more. A young mule'll last longer, but it has to be broke first."

"Which did he choose?" asked Mr. John.

"Guess," Arie said to Miss Nancy.

Miss Nancy grinned and handed Arie some more clay.

"He got a good deal on a young mule," said Cheever. "That meant he had to lead him home instead of ridin' him."

"I'm sensing another story here," said Miss Nancy.

"You're gettin' good at this," said Arie.

"By the time Wiley'd wrestled that mule up ta Clermont, he was plum tuckered out. He was sittin' by the road when the feller who sold them cold drinks up to your knees saw him. He pulled his truck over to help Wiley."

"Drinks up to your knees?" asked Miss Nancy.

"He's talkin' about the Nehi Cola Company," said Arie.

Cheever nodded. "That's what I said—Knee-High."

"I like those drinks," said Mr. John. Then he wrote something down in his notebook.

"Yeah," said Cheever. "They're good, especially the orange flavored ones. That feller felt sorry for Wiley, so he let him sit on the tailgate and lead the mule a mile or two. He drove real slow so Wiley could rest."

"That was nice of him," said Miss Nancy.

"It was," said Cheever. "Wiley was always partial to Knee-High drinks after that. He even talked Cleater into puttin' up a sign for 'em at his shop in Cleveland. It was right by the road, ya see."

"That's quite a story," said Mr. John. "But getting back to pottery, what did..."

Before he could finish his question, Lonzo started barking at a car that had pulled off the road down by the old chimney.

CHAPTER SEVEN

Cheever's Wife

"Hush Lonzo!" said Arie, as she turned around to look out the door.

"Customer's here," she said to Cheever.

Cheever leaned against the wall like he didn't want the people outside to see him. "Go see what they want," he said to Arie. "I want to tell Painter Man here another story."

"Oh, it's you they'll be wanting to gab with," said Arie, wiping her hands on her apron. "Always is."

Just then a boy about twelve and a girl my age ran into the shop. The girl was pretty.

Cheever was happy to see them, and that made me a little jealous. Still, I knew he wouldn't let them ride his mule or draw on any pottery while they were here, so it was all right.

"Why, hello there!" he said. "Come on in here."

"Do you remember us?" the boy asked Cheever. "From last year?"

Cheever rubbed his chin like he was thinking that over. "Let's see now," he said. Then he snapped his fingers. "You're that couple that was running off to Texas to rob banks waddn't ya? Bonnie and Clyde?"

I didn't know who Bonnie and Clyde were, but the pretty girl giggled like she did.

"No. I'm Billy," said the boy. "And this is my sister, Patti. We stopped here on our way home from Florida. You remember—you let us write our names on some...how do you say it, 'pott'ry' last year?"

The pretty girl added, "You said we could pick it up when we came back. So, here we are."

Cheever acted like he didn't remember. "Is that a fact?" he said, rubbing his chin.

They both bobbed their heads up and down. "Yep. So, here we are. All the way from Virginia."

"Virginia?" said Cheever, looking more puzzled than ever. "I never heard tell of such a place. You're makin' that up."

I *knew* he was teasing now. Everybody had heard of Virginia.

"No, we're not," insisted the boy. "It's a state. In America."

Cheever shook his head. "Naw. If we had a state named Virginia, I'd a heard about it. Don't you think so, Arie?"

"He's teasing you young'un's," Arie said. "Now, hunt up those pieces for 'em, Cheever."

When Cheever went into the back room, the pretty girl came over to see what I was doing.

"Whatcha drawing?" she asked.

"Daisies," I said, not looking at her. "I'm working here today."

"Do they pay you?"

"No. But I get to ride the mule."

"Yuck!" she said. "I hope it's not the one tied up outside. It smells awful!"

"He doesn't smell so bad."

"Yes, he does." She wrinkled her nose. That made her even prettier.

Then she asked, "Why are you drawing flowers on that?"

"Because that's what Aunt Arie wants. They're daisies." Then my face turned real red.

Before I could tell her I'd rather be drawing airplanes, Cheever came out of the back room. He was still pretending he couldn't find their pottery.

"Waddn't nothin' back there," he said. Then he walked over to a big churn on the table and picked it up. "Here it is! If it had been a snake, it'a bit me."

When they shook their heads no, Cheever picked up an even bigger churn. "It was this'n?"

The pretty girl giggled. "No, that's not right either." She pointed to a row of small pots on a shelf behind Cheever. "Ours are that size."

Cheever turned around to look at the shelf. "One of them little things? Are you sure?"

They both nodded yes.

Cheever reached for two little green cups. "Well, in that case, I reckon, these two here might do."

He handed the pieces to them. They seemed happy to see their names on them. "Let's show these to Mother!" she said. Then she grabbed Cheever's hand and pulled him to the door. "Come with us, Mr. Meaders. Mama wants to buy some 'pott'ry' to take to Florida as a gift for our aunt."

"Does she now? Well, I reckon I better go take care of

that little matter. Arie, you keep Painter Man and this woman entertained. I'll be back directly."

"No, you won't," said Arie.

Cheever stopped and turned his head. "What'd you say?"

"I said, stay as long as you want," Arie said louder.

"Aw-right then," said Cheever.

At the door, the pretty girl turned around and stuck out her tongue at me. Then she ran outside with her brother.

"Come on," Cheever said to Mr. John. "You've seen how I make pott'ry. Now let me show ya how I sell it."

I don't think Mr. John wanted to leave. But he put his drawing pad down, took his camera out of the bag and followed Cheever out anyway.

"I'll be back in a few minutes," he told Miss Nancy.

"Take your time," she said. "It'll give Mrs. Meaders and me a chance to visit."

I guess she didn't plan on visiting with me much.

"Howdy folks!" Cheever hollered to the people as he went outside. "What can I get up for ya?"

"Your husband is quite a salesman," Miss Nancy said to Arie, once they were gone.

"Why he's liable to be out there an hour," said Arie. "And that woman's gonna leave with more than one piece of pottery, too. But Cheever won't pressure her none. He always treats folks right—tries to anyhow."

Miss Nancy scooted her chair closer to Arie. "Mrs. Meaders, why don't we use this time to talk about you?"

"Not much to say," said Arie, leaning over to inspect the vase she was decorating now.

"Oh, I think there is," said Miss Nancy. She looked real close at the vase. "I really admire your work. It's beautiful."

Arie didn't say anything, but she seemed pleased.

"I understand you didn't start making pottery until…"

Miss Nancy stopped, like she'd said something wrong.

"Until I was too old for it?" asked Arie, laughing.

"No, no, I didn't mean that," said Miss Nancy.

I think she did, though.

"I ain't gonna fault ya none for tellin' the truth."

Miss Nancy put her hand on Arie's. "Would you mind telling me why you decided to start doing this?"

Arie thought for a minute. "Well, a while back, Cheever quit—decided he'd got too old for it. This shop was sittin' empty, and I got to wantin' it so bad, I just came up here and went at it."

"It must have felt natural to you. I mean, with you being around pottery most of your life."

Arie stopped working. "It did. But I could see things in my mind besides pitchers and churns. So, on my sixtieth birthday, I came up here, built me a little fire, and went to work at it. Hand me some more of that clay."

Miss Nancy broke off some clay from the ball and handed it to Arie.

"I'd worked up here a right smart," said Arie. "But I'd spent most of my time tendin' the house, choppin' cotton, workin' in the garden and such. I'd seen enough to know how pottery was made, though. Once I started, I kept at it and finally got to where I could turn. 'Course, lots of my early stuff went to the jar-pile."

"Why was that?"

"For one thing, the bottoms of my pieces would crack when we fired 'em."

"What made that happen?"

Arie got up and went over to the fan. She moved it a little so the air would blow on me more. I was glad because it felt good.

"Ya see," said Arie as she sat back down, "when I went

to take one off, I'd stop the wheel and pull the wire across the bottom. Cheever was watching me one day and said, 'you can't cut it off that-a-way. You got to hold the wire still and let the wheel keep turning.' I started doing it like that, and my bottoms didn't crack n'more."

"That's interesting," said Miss Nancy. "You're so talented, I find it extraordinary that you didn't create any pottery until you were sixty."

"Oh, I commenced decorating Cheever's pieces a good while before that. When I'd put grapes and leaves on his churns, people would pay five dollars for 'em. So, he'd let me do that."

Miss Nancy laughed. "I imagine so," she said.

Arie put a leaf on the vase and pressed it in place with her fingers. "Cheever can't make the things I vision. Then again, I can't make the things he sees in his head."

"We all have our own way of doing things," said Miss Nancy. "John says there are doers and those who sit on the sidelines and complain about what the doers are doing."

"Cheever's a doer all right," said Arie. She put the grape she'd rolled on the vase. "You plannin' on marryin' that feller?"

I leaned forward to hear the answer. I hoped it was no.

Miss Nancy laughed. "It took me a while to come around, but I am," she said.

"Good," said Arie. "You two fit together—sorta like me and Cheever."

Shoot, I thought. I guess it was back to Miss Presley for me. Or maybe that pretty girl outside.

"Tell me a bit more about how you started making pottery," said Miss Nancy. "I'd love to hear all about that."

"All right," said Arie. "Let's see how Emory's coming along with those daisies first." They both came over to my bench.

Miss Nancy seemed to like my drawings, but Arie frowned. "Well," she said, "those aren't bad. Still, I know you can do better."

She took a stubby pencil and some paper out of her pocket and drew a daisy on it. "Try to make it look like this one," she said.

Then she picked up a wet cloth and wiped my drawings off again.

Her daisy did look better than mine.

Miss Nancy smiled at me. Then she followed Arie back to the table. Arie sat down and started rolling another grape.

"At first, I'd make simple things like wall-hangers and such. People liked 'em, so I've started hand-building owls, quail, doves, chickens, and I don't know what all. I've even got it in my head to make an elephant sometime. Won't that be something?"

"It will," said Miss Nancy, as she went over to a shelf that had two of Arie's pottery chickens on it. "I love these roosters. They aren't only different, they're interesting and pretty, too."

Arie seemed pleased. "Thank you," she said. "I made one our old banty rooster didn't much like one time."

"Oh?" said Miss Nancy.

"Yeah. I fixed up a pretty good-sized rooster. After Cheever fired it, I took it down to the house and put it out in the flower bed. Well, after that, I couldn't keep the little banty rooster out of there to save my neck. You never saw such! He'd scratch and strut and do all he could to run that clay chicken off."

Miss Nancy thought that was funny. "What did you do?" she asked.

"I reckon the little feller thought his hens was gonna start steppin' out on him with it. I had to bring the pottery chicken back up here."

"That's funny," said Miss Nancy, sitting down by Arie. "What does Mr. Meaders think about your success as a potter?"

"I reckon he's made peace with it. When I first started foolin' with it, him and our boy, Lanier, got to wondering what I's a-doing up here."

Arie nodded towards a window. "They'd peep in that window there to see. I didn't let on like I saw 'em, though."

Miss Nancy laughed. "I wonder what they thought?"

"I didn't know, and I didn't care," said Arie. "Finally, Cheever couldn't stand it no more, and before long, he was back up here, too."

Miss Nancy, looked around the room. "So, you share the shop now?"

"We do. Lanier works here with us some. He likes to make old-style churns and pitchers like his daddy's. But they's just not much demand for that anymore."

"I'm curious," said Miss Nancy. "What do you call the type of pottery you make."

"I call it art pottery. Cheever calls it useless." Arie sighed. "He may be right."

Miss Nancy looked at the vase Arie had finished putting grapes on. "Beautiful things are never useless," she said.

Arie thought for a minute. "I reckon not. But, Cheever can turn four or five pitchers while I decorate one little ole somethin' or other."

I'd heard Granddaddy say the same thing.

"May I ask how you and Mr. Meaders met?" asked Miss Nancy.

"Oh, that ain't much of a story," said Arie. "Did you and your man meet up in Atlanta?"

"Yes. A mutual friend, Rosie Clark, introduced us. Believe it or not, she plays a funny witch on television named Miss Boo."

Wait a minute—she knew Miss Boo? I watched Miss Boo on television when I was little. I loved her!

"Really?" asked Arie. "Well, bein' introduced by a funny witch is a new 'n on me."

They both laughed. I kept thinking about Miss Boo. One time when we were in Atlanta, we saw her riding down the street tossing candy from her bicycle. I caught a little bag of red jelly beans.

I thought about telling Miss Nancy that, but she was already asking another question, and it wouldn't be polite to interrupt.

"So, how did you and Mr. Meaders meet? You must have a story, too."

Arie stopped working and sat back in her chair. "Well, my daddy's name was Rufus. He was a Waldrop, and he moved us down here from Franklin, North Carolina, in nineteen hundred and eleven. There was thirteen of us. We settled a little further down on Mossy Creek. Me and Cheever got to knowin' one another, and three years later, we married."

Arie wiped her hands and reached for more clay.

"So, you married into the pottery business?"

"I did. 'Course, that was about the time most potters was quittin' it."

"Why was that?"

"Tin cans. Glass jars was part of it, too. It took a while for those to catch on, though."

"Really?"

"Yeah. Folks was scared of glass jars, like they was the electricity at first. 'Course, that was a good thing for Cheever."

Arie leaned back in her chair. "At least for a while."

Miss Nancy raised her eyebrows. "People were afraid of glass?"

Arie chuckled. "Folks always look askance at anything new."

"I suppose that's true," said Miss Nancy. "I feel that way about the hula-hoop."

Arie looked at Miss Nancy. Then she went back to rolling grapes. I don't think she knew about hula-hoops.

Miss Nancy watched her. "Mrs. Meaders, if you don't mind my asking, what happened to Cheever's arm? I notice it doesn't bend right at the elbow. I hope that question's not too personal."

"Naw, it isn't," said Arie. "He fell out of a tree when he was eight or nine. It never did grow back right."

"That's terrible," said Miss Nancy. "He certainly hasn't let that arm hold him back."

"No, he hasn't," said Arie. She picked up a nail to make marks on a grape leaf she'd just put on. "Cheever's mother was supposed to be a Cherokee Indian. Maybe that's why he's so hard-headed."

"Really?" said Miss Nancy. "A Cherokee?"

Arie nodded. "Some of 'em claimed she was just half, though. And some said she was a white girl raised by Indians."

"Which do you think is true?" asked Miss Nancy.

"Law honey, I don't claim to know. I never met the woman. But I tell you one thing—her boys *loved* their mama—talked about her like she was a saint. The girls did, too."

"What happened to her?" asked Miss Nancy, as she watched Arie make marks on the leaf.

"She died not long after Johnnie Mae was born. Wiley was the oldest boy. He promised his mama on her deathbed that he'd not marry till her children were all grown."

I'd heard Granddaddy talk about that. Sometimes he cried when he did.

"Did Wiley keep his promise?"

Of course, he did. Granddaddy always kept his promises. I started to tell her that, but I kept quiet.

"He did," said Arie. "Wiley didn't marry till he was forty-two and already set in his ways."

"What an incredible story," said Miss Nancy. "Do you think any of your children will ever come back to this pottery business?"

"I doubt it," said Arie. "Lanier likes to dabble in it still. And our boy, Nub, comes down here ever' so often to make a pitcher or what-not. He ain't had much luck sellin' any of it, though. Pottery's a hard thing to make a livin' at nowadays."

Arie sat back in her chair. "Now, the grand-young'uns are a different story. They love coming up here and messing around with it."

Then Arie laughed. "One of 'em, Reggie's boy, David, even jumped out the school bus window when they wouldn't stop to let him out here."

Miss Nancy seemed surprised. "Really? Was he hurt?"

"No, he's a wiry little feller. And that bus was going pretty slow when it happened. I reckon the driver saw what he was fixin' to do before he did it."

I liked David. He was younger than me, but he sure knew how to have fun!

"Well, your style of pottery seems to be catching on," said Miss Nancy.

"Maybe so. Our boy, Nub, was here the other day wantin' me to show him how to make roosters."

"Did you?"

"Yeah, but I told him not to quit his job at the lumber yard yet."

They both laughed.

"Nub says he's thinking about making roosters and glazin' 'em blue," said Arie. "Whoever heard-tell of a blue rooster?"

"Who knows?" said Miss Nancy. Then she recited some sort of poem: *"I never saw a purple cow. I never hope to see one. But I can tell you anyhow, I'd rather see than be one."*

Arie laughed. "Maybe that goes for roosters, too. Don't brag on my decorated pieces when Cheever comes back in. Like I said, he thinks they're foolish."

"He might be jealous," suggested Miss Nancy.

Arie moved the vase she'd been working on to one side. "Maybe," she said. "I doubt it, though."

Arie turned around to look out the door. "Cheever feels like he's livin' in a world that don't need what he does n'more. That's what ails him."

CHAPTER EIGHT

Cheever's Jughead

Miss Nancy got up to look at one of Aunt Arie's glazed pieces on the back shelf. She was still looking when Cheever backed through the door, waving bye to the customers outside.

"Y'all stop by on your way home," he said. "I'll have ole Joe crow for ya again. I might even have him talkin' by then."

Mr. John followed Cheever through the door and put his camera back in its case.

Arie looked up. "They buy anything?" she asked.

"Ah, just one of your ole owls and that salt and pepper set—the one that didn't fire up right. What went with my pipe?"

"It's right over there where you left it," said Arie. "On the wedgin' table."

Cheever picked up his pipe. Then he noticed Miss Nancy looking at Arie's pottery.

"You ain't interested in them ole decorated pieces, are ya?" he asked.

"I can't help myself," said Miss Nancy, looking like she'd been caught eating a cookie before supper. "They're all so beautiful."

She sat back down by Arie again.

"Them decorated pieces are a waste of time and good clay both," said Cheever, shaking his head. "About like them jugheads some of 'em make."

That caught Mr. John's attention. He looked right at Cheever and said, "Have you ever thought about putting faces on your pieces? I've seen that done and find it quite interesting."

Cheever took the Prince Albert can out of his pocket and opened it. "Ah, I've fooled with 'em some—mighta made a half dozen or so. They take too long. And a jug with a face won't hold n'more than a jug without one."

Mr. John laughed, but he wanted to keep talking about jugheads. "Didn't they originate in Africa?"

Before Cheever could answer, Arie got up and started into the back room.

"Where you goin'?" Cheever asked her.

"I'll be back in a minute."

Cheever put his pipe back on the wedging table again instead of lighting it. "Aw, they's all sorts of stories about where them jugheads come from," he said. "Some say slaves brought the i-dee over from Africa, but I don't claim to know."

He walked to the door and looked out. "I remember one

of them things being at Grandpa's house when I was a boy. It was a great big ole jug, out on the porch. I guess some potter around here made it, but I don't know which one."

"Interesting," said Mr. John. "Well, I think they're excellent examples of artistic expression."

"Do you now?" said Cheever. "Well, I find 'em about as useless as a milk bucket under a bull."

That made me laugh. Mr. John and Miss Nancy didn't, though. So, I went back to drawing daisies. It was about time for Arie to wipe them off again anyway.

She came back from the other room carrying a dark-colored jughead about five inches tall. Cheever snorted when he saw it. "Where'd you dig that ole thing up from? I'd about forgot it was back there. I musta made that twenty years ago."

Mr. John took the jughead from Arie and held it out to look at. "That's one ugly looking fellow," he said, handing it to Miss Nancy. She took it, but I don't think she much wanted to.

"It *is* remarkable," she said. She handed it back real quick, though.

"Want to buy it?" Cheever asked her. "I'll let it go for three dollars."

Mr. John set it down by his bag. "I believe we'll pass on that," he said.

He still wanted to talk about jugheads, even if he didn't want to buy one. "I've heard the tradition dates all the way back to Egyptian times."

"Is that so?" asked Cheever. Seemed like he didn't care much one way or the other.

"Yes," said Mr. John. "They were supposed to ward off evil spirits. The idea was that the face would be so ugly the devil would stay away from the grave long enough to let the dead person's soul get to heaven."

Cheever picked up his pipe again This time, he lit it. "Yeah," he said, shaking the match and dropping it on the floor. "Sometimes cotton farmers used jugheads ta keep boll weevil poison in."

"Really?"

"That's what I've heard. And some folks kept whiskey in 'em to scare the young'un's off. That didn't work too good, though."

Cheever looked at me and winked, "I's always worried some cotton farmer'd get the jugs mixed up and get his-self drunk the hard way."

I thought that would end the jughead talk. It didn't, though.

"Did the face jugs you made have teeth?" asked Mr. John. "I've noticed some do and some don't."

"Depends," said Cheever.

"On what?"

"The funeral home, mostly."

"The funeral home?"

Miss Nancy turned around in her chair to look at Cheever.

"Yeah," he said, looking out the window. "It depends on how much business they have. Ya see, they can't take too many teeth from the same corpse, or the family can tell at the viewing."

Miss Nancy laughed.

"Don't pay him no mind," said Arie. "Potters pick out rocks for the teeth or make 'em out of clay, one or the other. They don't get teeth from no funeral home."

Mr. John seemed relieved to hear that.

"Well," said Cheever, blowing pipe smoke. "The funeral home makes a better story."

Mr. John turned to Arie. "Have you ever made any face jugs, Mrs. Meaders?"

"Not yet," she said. "I might try my hand at it someday. Mine won't have teeth, though—rock or otherwise."

"Thank goodness," said Miss Nancy.

"I did hear-tell of one good use for jugheads," said Cheever.

"Oh. What was that?"

Cheever winked at me, so I'd know he was fooling. "A feller in Clermont bought one to set atop his scarecrow."

"Did it work?"

"It did. Worked so well them crows brought back the corn they'd took the year before."

Everybody laughed but Arie. I think she'd heard that before.

"Don't egg him on," she said, without looking up.

Mr. John seemed to agree. "Let's change the subject then."

"Aw-right," said Cheever, looking towards the door. "But let's change it outside where there's more room. I gotta get ta grinding that clay, or Arie's gonna be outta anything to work with."

Cheever motioned for me to follow him outside. "Come on, boy. Surely you're done drawin' flowers by now."

I felt like telling him I'd finished three times already, but I didn't.

"You keep Emory off that mule," said Arie, as we started towards the door.

Since she didn't say anything about it, I didn't put my shoes back on.

CHAPTER NINE

Cheever's Circle

"You're lookin' good old son," Cheever said, as he untied Jason and patted his neck. Lonzo got up to stretch. Mr. John walked over to the pugmill and looked into the part that held the clay.

I was so excited, I couldn't keep still.

"I shoveled that raw clay in there this morning," said Cheever. "Look how pretty it is. That's Frank Miller clay."

"Frank Miller?"

"Yeah," said Cheever. "It comes from his place down the road a-ways—best clay there is. You mix with that with clay from two or three other places, and you got yourself some fine turnin' mud."

Mr. John took a picture of Frank Miller's clay.

Cheever puffed on his pipe for a minute. Then he led Jason to the pugmill and backed him up to the end of the big pole that lay on the ground.

When Cheever finished hooking Jason up, he took out his pipe. Then he looked at everything real good and motioned me over.

"I'm gonna need you to oversee this operation," he said. "The best place to do that is on this mule's back. Can you help me out with that?"

When I nodded, he swung me up on Jason's back.

I remember it so well. Cheever takes hold of Jason's bridle and starts us moving around the pugmill. He walks along, holding the bridle—the man's two steps matching the mule's four. Cheever and Jason carry on a conversation while they walk—"Come along, boy. A few more turns, and we'll go to the barn. Gonna mix this clay real good. Make some fine churns. Extra nubin' for you tonight. Come on, old son." Jason flicks his mule ears back and forth in reply.

"Watch your head there, Embo," Cheever said as we went under the overhead pole. We came to that pole twice each turn, so I had to duck pretty often.

I didn't mind. On that mule's back, I was the Lone Ranger, Roy Rogers, and Davy "Fess Parker" Crockett rolled into one hard-riding hero. That gentle ole mule had turned into a fiery horse with the speed of light, in a cloud of dust, and a hearty "Hi-yo Silver!"

I made-believe Cheever was a horse thief out to steal Trigger. I even took an occasional finger shot at him when he wasn't looking. Pow!

He caught me at it pretty often, though. When he did,

he'd slap his hands across his chest and pretend I got him right through the heart.

I saw Mr. John knock over an old wooden nail-keg beside the shop. I guess he was making sure it didn't have a wasp's nest under it. Then he sat down and opened up his drawing pad.

Just then, Arie came out the shop door with a pan of water. When she emptied it in the yard, it scared one of the chickens.

Arie saw me on the mule, but she went back inside without saying anything about it.

"What kinds of things did you make mostly?" Mr. John asked Cheever.

"Oh, a little bit of ever'thing," he said as we passed the nail keg. "Churns and pitchers, generally. I made lots of whiskey jugs, too."

"Whiskey jugs?" Mr. John looked up from his drawing pad.

"Aw, I meant to say syrup jugs," Cheever said, glancing back at me.

Mr. John started drawing again. "So, did you make many 'syrup jugs' over the years?"

He said syrup jugs kind of funny.

"I did," said Cheever, looking proud. "Folks generally wanted the one-gallon size. But I've turned five-gallon jugs, too. The ones that size was for haulin'."

"What did you call those?"

"Folks called 'em all kinds of things. One time a feller ordered a hundred 'milk jugs,' and he just had one cow."

Arie walked back outside with two unglazed vases. "And that cow had been dry for a year," she said.

Mr. John laughed but kept drawing.

"They never asked me how I made 'em," said Cheever, "and

I never asked them what they was gonna do with 'em. Waddn't my business. Come on, Jason. Walk this way. That'a boy."

"Tell him about the revenuer," Arie said, setting the vases on the table.

"What?" Cheever asked. He was making sure I ducked when we went under that overhead pole.

Arie turned around and spoke louder. "I said, tell him about the time that government man came by."

"Oh, yeah," said Cheever. He chuckled a little. "I about forgot about that."

"Sounds interesting," said Mr. John.

"Oh, it is," said Cheever. "That gov-meant man came snoopin' around tryin' to sniff out bootleggers. We musta had seventy or eighty 'syrup jugs' sittin' out on them tables over there."

"What did he do?" asked Mr. John, looking up.

"Weren't much he could do," said Cheever, "so he left. When he came back the next day, all them jugs was gone."

Just then, Miss Nancy came outside carrying one of Arie's bowls. She put it down by the pieces Arie had brought out and went over to see what Mr. John was drawing.

"What happened next?" Mr. John asked, as he showed Miss Nancy what he'd drawn. I wanted to see it, too, but not bad enough to get down off the mule.

Cheever and Arie laughed. "The gov-meant man asked where them jugs went in such a hurry," said Cheever. "I told him some feller bought 'em, but I didn't catch his name."

"It's a good thing, too," said Arie. "'Cause that feller's first name was 'The' and his last name was 'Sheriff.'"

"Arie," said Cheever, shaking his head. "You ain't gotta tell ever'thing you know."

"Lord help us if I do," Arie said real low, as she and Miss Nancy went back inside.

"Was it really the sheriff?" asked Mr. John, still drawing.

"I reckon the less said about that, the better," said Cheever.

"I agree," said Mr. John. "I imagine jugs holding a liquid of that sort would need to be impermeable."

"Naw," said Cheever. "That didn't matter much, but they couldn't leak. And mine didn't."

He looked back to see if I was okay. Except for the outlaws chasing me and Trigger, we were doing just fine.

"I remember makin' some jugs one time for a feller. He filled 'em up and put 'em in a holler log to pack out later. Then he took sick. He didn't get back up there for six weeks. When he did, he'd not lost a drop."

"So, none of that 'syrup' leaked out?"

"Nary a bit," said Cheever, looking pleased with himself. "I's always proud of that. Come on, Jason. We'll go to the barn after while. Gonna feed you extra tonight."

"Well, that's good," said Mr. John. "Now, moving on..."

Just then, Cheever quit walking. When Jason stopped, too, I bumped my head on the overhead pole. It didn't hurt much, though.

"Wait a minute," said Cheever. "I want to talk more about them syrup jugs not leaking."

"All right." Mr. John, closing his drawing pad and putting the pencil behind his ear.

Cheever looked serious. "Lots of potters couldn't make ware that didn't seep," he said. "That's important! Say you put up your picklin' meat in one that did. Why that meat would rot, and folks might not have enough to eat that winter. Whiskey's one thing but making a piece that might make some young 'un to go hungry is another."

Mr. John looked up at Cheever. "You know, Mr. Meaders, no one ever explained that to me before. I came here today thinking this is an interesting craft. But, you've really made me understand that what you do is much more than that."

Cheever clucked to Jason, and we started moving again.

Mr. John kept talking. "I just do my sketches and drawings for people in Atlanta," he said. "But you're up here making a real difference in people's lives."

"It was a good way to make a living," said Cheever. "But crocks and churns waddn't all we made. We made about anything a'body needed—cups, creamers, plates, all kinds of churns, flower pots, pitchers, even marbles for the young' uns. 'Course, I made a heap of thunder buckets, too."

"Thunder buckets?"

"He means chamber pots," said Arie, coming out the shop door with two more bowls. Then, looking at Cheever, she added. "Don't forget chicken jugs. You made a passel of them."

Miss Nancy stood in the shop door. "What in the world are chicken jugs?" she asked.

Cheever looked at Arie as we passed by. "You reckon it'll be aw-right to let 'em in on that?"

"I think so," said Arie.

"You've certainly piqued our interest," said Miss Nancy. "It wouldn't be fair to leave us hanging."

"I reckon not," said Cheever. "You use a chicken jug to water chickens. The way it works is top-secret, though. No tellin' what might happen if the Russians ever learned how to make chicken jugs."

Maybe if they did, they would send a chicken into space next time instead of a dog.

"I promise we won't breathe a word about it to the Russians," said Mr. John. "I was in the army, ya know."

"Ours or theirs?" asked Cheever.

"Cheever!" said Arie.

"Well, it don't hurt ta ask." Cheever stopped Jason again and looked at Mr. John. "Which one was it?"

"It was the U.S. Army," said Mr. John, laughing. "I promise. Do you want to see my discharge papers?"

"I reckon not," said Cheever, looking at Miss Nancy. "Long as she'll vouch for ya."

Miss Nancy moved a little closer so Cheever could hear better. "Well, I haven't actually *seen* his discharge papers, but I'm pretty sure he was on our side."

Cheever stopped Jason again and looked around the yard. "Aw-right then," he said. "We got a chicken jug laying around here somewhere, don't we, Arie? People don't ask for 'em like they used to."

"Yeah," she said. "Old man Cooley ordered that one in back a year ago. He ain't picked it up yet."

"Go get it and show it to 'em," said Cheever, clucking to Jason.

Arie went into the shop. While she was gone, Mr. John asked Cheever, "Do you ever sign any of your work?"

"Naw," he said. "Here lately, Arie's got ta puttin' my initials on a piece now and then. But, I ain't got time for such as that."

"Well," said Mr. John. "I sign my work."

"That's different," said Cheever. "You're an artist."

He looked at Cheever real close. "So are you," he said. "In every sense of the word."

Cheever didn't agree. "Pshaw," he said. "The stuff I make is to *use*, not sit somewhere and look pretty. That may be what folks want nowadays, but I'm too old to fool with it. Besides, I could tell a piece of my work if I was to see it in China—signed or not."

"What about your brothers' work? Would you know their pottery if you saw it in China?"

Cheever rubbed his chin. "Well, maybe not in China," he said. "I hear they's lots of pott'ry over there."

"Well," said John, "would you know your brothers' work anywhere else?"

"Sure, I would," said Cheever. "Ever' one of 'em had their own style."

"How so?"

"It might be how they put a handle on, or the shape of a piece, or maybe by the lip. Take Wiley—his pott'ry was always thin. Thin and light. Customers liked that."

Cheever looked around a minute. Then he stopped Jason and went over to pick up a churn. "Feel this," he said.

Mr. John hefted the churn.

"That's a right light piece," said Cheever. "But if Wiley'd made that, it'd be lighter by a third."

Cheever sat the churn down. Then he came back and started walking Jason again.

"We used ta tease Wiley and say that he made it thin to keep from havin' to get up so much clay. He could get more pott'ry out of a wagon-load than anybody."

"How did he do that?"

"Wiley has great, long arms so he could pull up real tall pieces. Him and Ka-zee both."

"Did you and your brothers dig your own clay?" Mr. John asked.

Cheever scratched his head. "How else would we get it?"

Mr. John wrote something down. Then he asked, "Did it all come from the Frank Miller farm?"

"Lord, no," said Cheever. "We got it from all over the place. I still do."

"How do you know where to find it?"

"Oh, it's usually along a stream bed somewhere. "Sometimes you can see it along the creek bank. Other times, you just get a feelin' about it. When you find a good lode, you keep diggin' in it till it peters out. Then you find yourself another vein."

Mr. John looked up at Cheever. "What about glazes? Do you make your own?"

"Mostly," said Cheever. "I'll tell you one thing—potters can come up with more glazes than you can shake a stick at. Ever' potter has his favorite."

"What's yours?"

Cheever studied for a minute. "I've always favored ash glaze. We make that outta ashes from the kiln and what-not. It's easy to mix up and makes a right pretty pot."

Just then, Arie came out with the chicken jug. She pointed to the opening in front and said, "Look here. See? That's where the chicken puts his head to drink."

Mr. John got up from the nail-keg and walked over to look. Cheever looked at me and winked. I didn't wink back. Me and Trigger were in Comanche Country, and I needed to keep my eyes open.

"So, you only fill the jug up to there?" Mr. John asked. He pointed to the opening near the bottom.

"No," said Cheever. "That's the top-secret part. You fill it all the way up, but the water won't leak from that hole down at the bottom. Took me twenty years and two trips to Washington, D.C. to learn that."

"I imagine it would," said Mr. John. Then he sat back down. "Maybe that's why those presidents keep stopping by here."

"Could be," said Cheever. "Don't let that get out, though."

Arie sat the chicken jug by Mr. John.

He seemed more interested in Cheever than the jug. "In addition to operating this pottery shop, you did some farming, didn't you?"

"Ever' body did," said Cheever. "Had to."

"What did you grow?"

"We growed cotton and enough corn to keep the cow and mule fed—hogs, too. And we always had some left over for us to mill."

"We always had a big garden, too," said Arie. "Still do."

"And my little goober patch," said Cheever. "I do like my peanuts."

Cheever reached in his pocket and tossed a peanut to Mr. John as we passed. He caught it with one hand. I guess he really had been in the Army.

"Cheever!" said Arie, "I told you not to give him the ones outta your pocket."

Miss Nancy reached for Mr. John's hand and pulled him up. "Come inside with me," she said. "I want to show you a pitcher Mrs. Meaders made."

She picked up the chicken jug and started inside, leading Mr. John by the arm.

"I'll go in with ya," said Arie. "It's hot out here." Then she looked at Cheever. "You might oughta get Emory out of the sun for a spell."

"Let me get Jason over to that shady spot," he said. When he did, he helped me down and tied the reins to a pole.

"You rest right here, old son," he said, rubbing the mule's face. "You done good. Yes, sir, you did. You nibble some of that-there grass and rest a spell."

I patted Jason's nose, too, and told him we'd be right back.

The fan inside the shop felt good. So, I stood in front of it and held my arms out wide. Just then, a car horn honked. Even Cheever heard it.

"I swanee," he said, "I can't make pott'ry for sellin' it. Let me go see what those folks want."

When Cheever got to the door, he turned around. "Aw,

Arie, it's them folks from Clarkesville that ordered that canister set the other day. They'll be wantin' you, not me." He went over to the wall and leaned against it.

Wiping her hands on her apron, Arie walked to the door. "Come with me, Cheever," she said. "They might need a churn, too. Anyhow, they'll want to talk to you."

"What would anybody driving a Cadillac car want with a churn?"

"You never can tell," said Arie. "Come on."

Cheever looked at his guests.

"Go ahead," said Mr. John. "We'll stay in here and visit with Emory."

Cheever laid his pipe on the shelf beside the wheel.

As soon as he and Arie went outside, Mr. John picked up the chicken jug. "Emory," he said, like he was telling me a secret. "Do you want to see if this really holds water?"

I knew it did. We had one at our house. But Granddaddy says you have to humor city people sometimes.

He walked to the door and peeked out. Seeing Cheever and Arie busy with the customers, he took the jug to the foot-tub. Then he held it down in the water sideways. After it filled up, he sat it on the shelf by the wheel.

Him and Miss Nancy looked to see if any water spilled out. They seemed tickled when it didn't. They were still looking when Cheever came back in.

"I told you that's top-secret stuff," he said. Cheever pretended to be real serious. "You sure you ain't a spy?"

Mr. John grinned. "Quite sure. But, if I was, I'd have to report back that this is pretty interesting."

"Not to a chicken," said Cheever, laying two peanuts on my bench.

"I suppose not," said Mr. John, going over to his bag to get his notebook out.

"Did those folks want a churn?" Miss Nancy asked. She went over to the door and looked out at Arie and the folks from Clarkesville.

"Naw," he said. "Folks like them only make over Arie's things. The more useless somethin' is, the more they want it."

"I don't suppose they see it that way," she said. "Anyway, I'm amazed at how many things you can make from clay, and at how useful it was...I mean is."

Cheever looked at her. But he didn't say anything.

She looked out the door again. "I mean, people quite literally could not have lived without what you produced here."

Cheever looked around for his pipe. When Miss Nancy pointed to it, he picked it up off the shelf.

"Folks that *need* this stuff are gettin' scarce," he said. He lit his pipe. "So are potters—ones like me, anyhow."

Cheever looked out the door at the people buying Arie's pottery. He seemed sad. "This place was more'n a pott'ry shop, ya know."

"How so?" asked Mr. John.

"It was a gatherin' place, too. Why, all sorts of folks would congregate here. Sometimes the yard would be full of 'em."

"You mean your neighbors?" asked Mr. John.

"Neighbors, and folks from Cleveland, too. Anybody runnin' for office would come by to let us know about it first. They always wanted me to support 'em before they announced. That's 'cause I had so many friends, ya know. And I knew a lot of people."

Cheever studied his pipe for a minute. "This handmade pott'ry is gonna be gone after while. When nobody's makin' it n'more, people will forget how it's done."

Just then, Arie backed through the door, waving bye to her customers. Then she put some money into her apron pocket.

"They buy much?" Cheever asked.

"Just that canister set."

"And I saw them load up two owls," Miss Nancy said. "Don't forget those."

Arie looked away. I don't think she'd planned to mention those owls.

"They didn't have room for a churn," she said, sitting back down.

Cheever shook his head. "Yeah, them Cad-E-Lacs ain't got no trunk space a-tall." He studied his pipe for a minute. "Anything useful ain't in style n'more. Anyhow, them folks wouldn't know what to do with a churn if they had one."

Cheever looked sad for a minute, but then he got happy again. "I got another story for ya," he said to Mr. John. "You'll like this one, too, Embo. It's about your granddaddy's still."

I didn't know Granddaddy'd ever had a still. He sure hadn't mentioned that to me.

"Your brother, Wiley, had a still?" asked Mr. Kollock.

"Well," said Cheever, "he didn't really have one, but he wanted one awful bad."

"I don't understand."

Cheever and Arie both laughed. "Since we was makin' so many syrup jugs, Wiley came up with the i-dee of makin' something to go in 'em. So, he talked Ka-zee into helpin' him set up a still."

I stopped working on my daisies to listen.

Cheever pushed his cap further back on his head. "Ya, see, they wanted to make 'em some money. But they's both scared to death of the law. So, they decide ta put the still in the kitchen of that old house."

Cheever pointed out the shop door towards the house across the road.

"In the kitchen?" asked Mr. John.

"Yeah," said Cheever. "They tore up the floor and went to diggin' 'em out a place. Pa saw 'em working at it and asked what they's doin', and they told him."

"What did he say?"

Arie laughed. "He told 'em the same thing anybody would have. That it was too close to the road. People passin' would smell the mash cookin'. Not to mention, it'd likely burn the house down."

"I see," said Mr. John. "What did they do?"

Arie turned around and said, "What Cheever did makes a better story."

"Oh?" asked Mr. John. "What happened?"

Cheever looked at me and grinned. "You ain't gonna tell your granddaddy I told this on him, are you?"

I shook my head no. I wanted to hear this.

"Let me tell it," said Arie. "Wiley and Ka-zee decided they'd move the thing down to the creek. Cheever was just a whipper-snapper then. Anyhow, about the time they got it set up, him and two of the Dorsey boys snuck off down there with their guns."

Mr. John looked surprised. "I take it you were opposed to the still, Mr. Meaders?'

"Naw," said Cheever. "We just wanted to scare 'em some. You know how boys are."

"What did you do?" asked Miss Nancy.

Arie started laughing. "They waited till Wiley was about ready to crank it up, and then Cheever and them started shootin' up in the air and yelling, 'REVENUERS!

YOU'RE ALL UNDER ARREST!' Like to scared 'em to death."

That *was* funny. But they shouldn't have scared Granddaddy that way.

"They didn't go back down to that creek for a week," Arie said. "Maybe two."

"Did you ever tell them it was you?" Mr. John asked Cheever.

He laughed. "Lord, no. I might not be smart, but I ain't stupid." He leaned back against the wall and puffed on his pipe. I think he'd about quit working for the day.

Mr. John dropped his pencil. It rolled under the chair. "How long did Wiley make pottery?" he asked when he found it.

"He quit makin' during the war," said Cheever. "His last boy was fixin' to go in the service, ya see, and there waddn't gonna be nobody to help him n'more. Plus, he was nearly seventy-years-old then."

"Tell him about that last batch Wiley made," said Arie.

"I'd about forgot about that," said Cheever.

"What happened?" Mr. John asked.

Cheever blew some pipe smoke before he answered. "The week before his boy, Ray, was gonna leave for the Army, the two of 'em made up a big batch of churns and what-not. Wiley was gonna shut his shop down after that to go in the chicken business."

"The poultry business did start booming about then," said Mr. John.

Cheever didn't hear him. He kept talking.

"When they finished, Ray decided it'd be a good i-dee to put that batch up somewhere. Just keep it, ya know—for the family and such, since it'd be the last Wiley'd ever make."

"That *was* a good idea. Did they do that?"

"Wiley didn't much want to—he'd made that pott'ry to sell, ya see—but he finally agreed to it. Turned out not to make much difference, though."

"Why was that?"

"It come a hard freeze that night," said Cheever. "Ever' piece of it busted. I always hated that for Wiley."

That made me feel bad for Granddaddy, too.

"Tell me about your brother, Caulder," Mr. John said to Cheever. "I haven't been able to find out much about him."

"Caulder was a pretty rough ole boy," said Cheever. "All my brothers were, really. But Caulder was the wildest. He was hard to get along with—especially after he lost his hand."

"Things can be difficult with brothers," says Mr. John.

"Yeah," said Cheever. "I reckon Sears didn't always get along with Roebuck."

Mr. John wrote that down. "How did Caulder lose his hand?"

I knew that. I'd heard Granddaddy talk about it a lot.

"Fell through the floor of a boxcar," said Cheever. "Out in Montana. Got it cut off clean to the elbow. He used a pincher-hook for a hand after that. It was a real mean-looking contraption."

Granddaddy had a picture of Caulder holding up a stringer of fish with that hook. It was scary looking. I wondered if he had that hook on when they buried him.

I was about to ask Cheever that. But just then, Arie stood up and put a piece of plastic over the ball of clay on her table. She took out the money from her apron pocket and handed it to Cheever. "Put this in your pocket. And don't lose it."

Then she hung her apron on the nail and dusted off her dress.

"I won't," said Cheever, stuffing the money into the pocket with his French harp.

Arie looked at the visitors. "Y'all stay as long as ya want," she said. "But I gotta start supper."

"We've got to be running along ourselves," said Mr. John, standing again. "I can't tell you how much we've enjoyed meeting you both." He looked at me. "You too, Emory."

Arie motioned for me to come to where she was standing by the foot-tub. "Grab your shoes and come over here," she said. "You need to wash your feet off before your mama sees 'em."

The water felt good when I stepped in the bucket. Arie made me rub my feet till the dirt came off. Then she put down a clean rag for me to step on and dry them off.

While I put my shoes and socks back on, Mr. John held out his hand to Cheever. "We'll certainly be looking forward to another visit real soon."

"Me, too," said Cheever, shaking his hand.

Miss Nancy walked over and hugged Arie. I don't think she expected that because she said, "Oh, dear," and sort of stepped back.

Miss Nancy stepped back, too. Then she picked up the magazine with Cheever's picture on it. "Don't forget to sign this for me," she said to Arie. She looked at Cheever when she said that, though.

He pretended not to hear her and picked up a piece of clay he'd dropped on the floor.

"Cheever ain't much for autographs," said Arie. Then she asked Miss Nancy, "Do you have a pen? I don't want to sign it in pencil."

Miss Nancy shook her head no and looked at Mr. John. "But he does. He's had a pen in his pocket since the day I met him."

He did, too, so he took it out and handed it to Arie.

"Thank you for today," Miss Nancy said, while Arie wrote on the magazine. "It was a pleasure spending this time you."

"Oh, it was our pleasure," said Arie, handing Mr. John back his pen. "I hope you got what you came for."

"Even more," said Miss Nancy. "I think John got lots of information for any future projects he might decide to do— some good pictures, too."

Arie gave Miss Nancy her magazine back and came over to see my daisies. I thought she'd wipe them off again, but she didn't.

"Now that's more like it," she said, brushing a fleck of clay off the little vase with her finger. "Good job! You even drew 'em on both sides."

I felt myself turning red again, but it was a good feeling.

She patted me on the head. "Your mama'll likely collect you before supper. If she don't, you come down to the house and eat with us."

"Yeah," said Cheever. "We're having a two-course meal—cornbread and milk."

Arie shook her head. "Nancy, John, y'all are welcome to eat with us, too," she said. "What Cheever said's not so. The garden's in. We got more vegetables than we know what to do with. Why, I cut a peck of okra this morning before breakfast."

"Thank you," said Miss Nancy. "But I promised John I'd cook him supper tonight at his cabin."

Arie leaned over, and I heard her whisper, "I guess he wants to see if you can cook."

Then she spoke in her regular voice again. "I hate to leave, but supper ain't gonna cook itself." She picked up the plate with the two teacakes and walked out the door. "Bye now," she said, waving. "I hope to see you both again real soon."

Miss Nancy came over and looked at my pot. "Those daisies are perfect," she said. "I can't wait to see this all fired and glazed pretty. Maybe, one day, I can help you put real flowers in it."

I managed to nod and say I'd like that, too.

"Don't be a stranger, Painter Man," said Cheever. "I got lots more stories to tell ya, and some of 'em are true."

That made Mr. John laugh. "I'm sure you do," he said. "And I can't wait to hear them." Once he'd made sure everything was back in his bag, he swung it over his shoulder.

Just as they got to the door, Cheever grabbed the pan of peanuts. There were only a few left, but he held the pan out. "Here. Take the rest of these with ya."

"Oh, thank you," said Mr. John, holding out both hands. "We'll eat these on the way to Clarkesville."

Cheever poured the peanuts into Mr. John's hands. "Eat till you bust," he said, slapping the empty pan against his leg.

When we got outside, the sun wasn't as bright as it was last time.

At the beginning of my life, I was given the opportunity to witness something incredible. A master craftsman whose world was vanishing in front of his eyes, and mine. Cheever's way of life was almost gone, but I didn't know that. He saw it as plain as day. But as an eight-year-old boy, I was too young to know.

Mr. John and Miss Nancy started down the driveway. Cheever took my slingshot out of his pocket. "Here ya go, boy," he said, handing it to me. "Don't load this thing again till you get home."

As we stood in the doorway watching them leave, Cheever put his hand on my shoulder. "You ready to ride Jason back to the barn, Embo?"

I nodded. My tail was a little sore, but I still had another trail ride left in me.

About halfway to the car, Mr. John stopped and gave the peanuts to Miss Nancy.

After dusting his hands off on his pants, he looked at ole Joe. "Mr. Meaders?" he called out. "May I try something before I go?"

"Help yourself," said Cheever.

Mr. John cupped his hands around his mouth and yelled, "Crow, Joe!"

Ole Joe didn't crow, though. The hens clucked and cackled, but he didn't make a sound.

EPILOGUE

After Cheever's funeral in November of 1967, one of his neighbors summed up his death this way: "Cheever's passing was like a giant oak falling—the whole community felt it."

So, it wasn't just me.

Cheever's wife, my Great-Aunt Arie, lived another twenty-two years. She kept making and decorating her pottery as long as she was able. By the time she died, in 1989, many of her pieces were selling for thousands of dollars at auctions like Sotheby's in New York.

Cheever's pottery also increased in value, and soon collectors from across the country scrambled to obtain it.

Cheever and Arie's second son, Lanier, kept making his famous face jugs and other pottery for thirty years after Cheever died. Along with that of his mother and father, Lanier's pottery was also displayed at the Smithsonian Institution.

In their later years, four of Cheever and Arie's eight children— John, Edwin, Reggie, and Ruby—did indeed take up the craft of pottery again, establishing their own shops and styles.

And, yes, Edwin (Nub) did rather well glazing his roosters blue.

John Kollock worked in Atlanta a few more years, but the lure of the mountains grew too strong. He moved to Habersham County and became famous for his writing, love of theatre and for painting more historically accurate pictures of Northeast Georgia than we can count.

Two of them, *Blasting Off* and *An Early Start—1915* depicted Cheever's kiln and that old family home across

from the shop. The cover of this book—Cheever's pugmill—
is another John Kollock original.

Of course, before all that happened, or maybe because
of it, he married Miss Nancy Rigg.

Now, let's flash forward forty-two years from that day
in 1958—give or take a month—to the surprise fiftieth
birthday party my wife had for me.

During that party, I got a phone call from my Aunt
Barbara, Mother's baby sister. Barbara asked me to come to
her house. She said she had a birthday present for me.

I didn't go for a few days—I guess I was expecting a
shirt or something—but when I did, Barbara went to a shelf
and took down a little vase with daisies crudely drawn on
two sides.

Then she put it in my hands.

That day at Cheever's shop came back in a flood of
memories that ultimately resulted in this book.

"I drew those," I said, holding the vase like the treasure
it was.

"I know you did. I wondered if you'd remember."

"How on earth do you have this?"

Barbara smiled her Barbara smile. "I was in the shop a
few weeks after you drew those. Arie had taken it out of the
kiln that day along with some other things. She asked me to
keep it for you until you were old enough to appreciate it. I
decided I'd wait till you turned fifty. I've enjoyed it for
years, and now it's yours."

That little grey vase is my most prized possession.

I'll always be grateful to Aunt Barbara for keeping it
safe. She is a sweet woman. So was Arie.

So is Nancy, who—sixty years later—did indeed help
me fill Aunt Arie's little vase with flowers.

Becky Peebles

ACKNOWLEDGMENTS

No one writes a book alone. At least no one I know. Maybe the Great Ones do, but not me. So many folks helped with this effort, my mind won't even pretend to remember them all, even if my heart does.

First, there's my wife, Judy. As I type this, she's reading the bulk of this manuscript for the first time, sitting in our living room by the fire. She'll tell me if what I've written is good or bad. I trust her completely.

It's April 22, 2018, a rainy Sunday afternoon here on Yonah Mountain—as a rule, my favorite kind of day.

Except this is not a great day for us because it may be the last one for our beloved, beautiful black cat of eighteen years, Sylvester. During those years, I've only typed a handful of words without him lying nearby.

But Sylvester's not here in my office as I type these lines today. He's down at the house, sleeping fitfully in Judy's lap while she reads, cries and softly caresses his fur. I spent the last hour doing the same thing. Sylvester has been a part of every book I've written, and now he's part of this one, too.

Besides Judy and Sylvester, I want to thank my friend, Billy Chism—an honest critic whose opinion I value. Sometime in the next few days, I'll hand him this manuscript, and it will be better because he read it.

No less valued is Ann Willis, a native of England and an honorary Southerner, who appreciates our language in a special way.

Nancy Kollock is another special friend. She is the wife of the late, great John Kollock. Her memories of visits to Cheever and Arie's shop have proven as invaluable as her husband's priceless paintings.

Numerous members of my family, the Meaders family—my mother's people—have helped and encouraged me. I can't list them all, but four, I can't leave off: Lenore, Jessie, Ruby, and Whelchel.

Linda Jordan, a friend of many years and a woman with a great ear for Appalachian dialects, has played a great role in this project. Thank you, Linda.

I can't forget Michelle Ash, who helped me find my eight-year-old voice. Again.

Then there's Bill House, listed on the legal page as William M. House, under "legal review by." He's more than a lawyer, he's a friend—and a good one. It doesn't hurt that he loves pottery as much as I do.

I also want to thank my dear friends, Mike and Ann Banke, two people who love North Georgia and its history. Without them, I never would have written a play version of my first novel, *The Valley Where They Danced*. They played a big role (pun intended) in the play version of this book as well.

I want North Georgia artist, Becky Peebles, to know how much I appreciate her talent and skill in providing the illustrations for this book.

The book by Ralph Rinzler, *The Meaders Family of Mossy Creek,* has been an invaluable resource and the source of many of Cheever and Arie's actual quotes.

I also owe a lot to my friend Dr. John Burrison, who always insists I call him John, without the doctor part. Dr. Burrison's books *Brothers in Clay* and *From Mud to Jug* are wonderful references I use time and time again. So, thank you, John.

To everyone else: you know who you are. My heart remembers you, too.

ABOUT THE AUTHOR

Emory Jones grew up in White County, Georgia in the southern Appalachians. He has been the Southeastern editor for *Farm Journal* magazine and executive vice president at an Atlanta based advertising agency. During his career, Emory interviewed and wrote about farmers in all 50 states. He has written five other books including *White County 101, Zipping Through Georgia on a Goat Powered Time Machine, Heart of a Co-Op—The Habersham EMC Story, Distant Voices—The Story of the Nacoochee Valley Indian Mound* and *The Valley Where They Danced*. Emory has also written and had two plays produced—one based on his book, *The Valley Where They Danced,* and another adapted from this book called *Cheever*. He and wife, Judy, live on Yonah Mountain near Cleveland, Georgia.